THE BACKGROUND OF ASTRONOMY

BY HENRY C. KING

The History of the Telescope

THE BACKGROUND
OF
ASTRONOMY

*

HENRY C. KING

PH. D, M. SC, F.R.A.S, F.B.O.A.

*Senior Lecturer in the Department of Ophthalmic Optics
Northampton Polytechnic, London*

WATTS

40 DRURY LANE LONDON WC2

First published in 1957
by C. A. Watts & Co, Ltd,
40 Drury Lane, London, WC2

Printed in Great Britain
in 12 pt. Fournier type
by Richard Clay & Company Ltd
Bungay, Suffolk

TO MY MOTHER

*

* CONTENTS *

∗ PREFACE ∗

THE following pages outline the story of astronomy from its obscure beginnings in the Near East to its position at the close of the sixteenth century in Western Europe. Their purpose is largely to dispel the general idea that the findings in this earlier period were less stimulating than those which followed the invention of the telescope. Early achievements in astronomy were of course entirely different in character from those which followed Galileo's discoveries with optical means. Their essential dependence on naked-eye observation alone set definite restrictions on the nature and scope of physical enquiry. Even so, one dominating task emerged—that of uncovering the geometrical framework which underlies the striking periodicities in the motions of the heavenly bodies—and occupied the best minds in astronomy and geometry for over two thousand years. The story of this particular quest will perforce form an important but by no means major part of my text. It began in the last centuries B.C., when Chaldean astrologer-priests succeeded in producing a purely algebraic planetary theory. It ended early in the seventeenth century, when Kepler abandoned forever the Greek concept of uniform motion in circular orbits and assigned the earth and other planets to the elliptical orbits of the heliocentric system. I shall, however, give only the general outline of these developments, for the ingenious geometrical expedients used by Eudoxus, Hipparchus, Ptolemy, Copernicus, and others have already been described in sufficient detail elsewhere. I have constantly borne in mind my original aim of writing a popular sketch for readers who have no special scientific training and yet desire to understand how astronomy grew into a great and fascinating science.

The fact that throughout this long period the sun, moon, and five then-known planets acquired the successive natures of celestial deities, divine animals, and heavenly influences, necessitates

I

frequent reference to religious beliefs and also to the pseudo-science of astrology. Astronomy arose, we are told, because early man saw in the punctual sun and moon the only way of telling the progress of time. Yet this temporal need was by no means the only spur to astronomical observation. No less important was his desire to worship something greater than himself, for this found its expression in early fertility cults, which often involved particular reference to the moon and later to the entire host of heaven.

In Mesopotamia, and as primitive local cults fused into one great polytheistic religion, the sun, moon, and planets became identified with powerful national deities. As the planets wandered against the starry background they were regarded as divine actors in a celestial drama which involved the fate of kings and nations. The astrologer-priests of Babylon and other important religious centres not only offered prayers and paid tribute to these divine luminaries, but from temple towers kept an ever-watchful eye on their relative dispositions and appearances in the wheeling heavens. In this way there grew up a comparatively accurate knowledge of the cyclic changes in the motions of the planets, which, despite the undermining influence of old traditions, almost ripened into a full and independent science.

By about the fourth century B.C., Chaldean astrology, with rich infusions of divination, magic, and sorcery, had begun to percolate into the Greek world. It rose into some prominence during Roman times, and blossomed into sterile maturity during the last centuries of our period. For princes and prelates alike it justified the time and money spent on astronomy, then generally regarded as its otherwise useless handmaiden. It had close connections with what we would now call chemistry, meteorology, and medicine, the more so because in early times these activities lacked their present distinctions. Immense effort went into the preparation of planetary tables, which more often than not served no other purpose than to increase the supposed accuracy of astrological predictions. By the end of the sixteenth century, however, it was already in slow decline, and Kepler for one could label it the 'foolish little daughter of the respectable, reasonable mother astronomy'.

The belief that appearances in the heavens govern or at least condition events on the earth kept men's eyes strained upwards ; it also clouded their judgements. Whenever the more credulous among them witnessed the zodiacal light or displays of aurorae they heard the clash of arms and saw the shaking of spears, swords, and shields. Eclipses, comets, meteors, and planetary conjunctions were invariably regarded as omens of disaster. Those who seldom observed the heavens from one year to the next were usually the loudest in their utterances when anything unusual appeared. Comets shed pestilence and famine, multiple planetary conjunctions indicated the end of the world, and novae or 'temporary stars' augured the overthrow of kingdoms. Even when the cosmos was stripped of most of its medieval moral garb and made subject to the reign of physical law, the love of the marvellous persisted in beliefs in the plurality of worlds and in possible cometary collisions with the earth. Today its deep roots inspire the pseudo-scientific extravagances of interplanetary travel and accounts of flying saucers and visitors from other planets. Something of the earlier stages of this curious background will appear in the following pages. It conditioned astronomical thought for many centuries and its depressing doctrines were not abandoned until men ceased to interpret experience in terms other than those of the supernatural.

No assessment of early astronomy would be complete without reference to its connections with mathematics. The use of calendars in ancient times for fixing festivals and agricultural activities implies not only reasonable accuracy in observation but considerable ability in numeration. Greek progress in geometry enabled Eudoxus and Hipparchus to turn astronomy into a mathematical science. Well before the Christian era the Greeks had discovered that the earth is round, Eratosthenes had made a fair estimate of its size, and Aristarchus of Samos had calculated the distances of the sun and moon. Its crowning triumph came when Ptolemy in the

3

second century A.D. formulated a geocentric planetary system which reigned supreme for above fourteen centuries.

Astronomy also had early interconnections with geography, map-making (cartography), and navigation. The need for accurate latitude values did much to keep its observational aspect alive in places remote from established centres of scientific activity. The problems of longitude determination, which towards the end of our period focused attention on the motion of the moon and the positions of the fixed stars, were eventually solved by contributions from horology. Also on the practical side was the science of perspective which was cultivated both as a derivative of mathematics, and after the invention of spectacles about A.D. 1300, as a craft. From the latter aspect emerged the microscope and telescope, two aids to human vision which broke down the respective barriers of size and distance.

Our story opens with a general picture of the main astronomical ideas which arose in ancient Mesopotamia and Egypt. During this long period of at least three thousand years, the work of successive generations of priests produced an abundance of data regarding the more outstanding motions in the heavens. Observing methods were simple in the extreme, and even at their best involved no more than the use of sighting devices and shadow- and water-clocks. The stars were grouped into constellations; they became invested with occult significance, were probably used to orientate monuments and temples, and gave clues as to the progress of the seasons. In Mesopotamia, particular attention was given to star groupings frequented by the planets, and the notion of the twelve signs of the zodiac apparently originated there at a very early date. The most productive centuries were undoubtedly those just before the Christian era, when rules for predicting the positions of the planets emerged and gave a new significance to astronomical observation. But by this time free-thinking philosophers in Ionia and on the Greek mainland had established new and more fruitful methods of interpreting celestial appearances.

The study of Greek ideas and achievements takes us from

4

Ionia and the Greek provinces to Athens and thence to Alexandria. The reader is introduced to the enlightened rationalism and speculations of Thales, Anaxagoras, Pythagoras, Plato, Aristotle, and many others, and in the account of Hipparchus and other investigators of the first Alexandrian school, sees something of the finest achievements of Greek science.

The Roman scene is sketched in Chapter VII which also contains some idea of Ptolemy's massive contributions to astronomy, astrology, geography, and optics. With the fall of Alexandria to the Arabians in A.D. 642, the Greek heritage was absorbed at new centres in the Orient. Chapter VIII accordingly takes us to Damascus, Baghdad, Khorasan, and Samarcand, covers a period of some eight hundred years, and deals with the scientific and literary labours of Arabians, Syrians, Persians, and Mongols. The somewhat faltering course of later Muslim astronomy ended in the fifteenth century with the death of the learned Ulugh Bey, by which time new and important developments were in progress in Western Europe.

As Chapter IX plainly shows, the first task of twelfth-century European scholars was to translate and absorb something of the vast Graeco-Arabic intellectual heritage which came to them *via* Moslem Spain. Arabic versions of Ptolemy were studied with enthusiasm, but nothing was done to test or improve upon his findings. After the fall of Constantinople in 1204, Greek versions of Aristotle's scientific writings became available, and before long his cosmology was an important part of Church doctrine. Astrology masqueraded as a science and had strong associations with medicine and chemistry. Since perfectly natural events were assigned to supernatural causes, impressive phenomena like comets, bright meteors, and planetary conjunctions bred all manner of strange fancies. In contrast to this depressing level of astronomical thought, the practical activities introduced in Chapter X show that there was still some measure of hope for its future. The first mechanical clocks appeared in the thirteenth century, Alfonso X at Toledo drew up new planetary tables but added no fresh observational material, and a group of scholars at Oxford drew attention to the merits of practical investigations in optics.

The fifteenth century witnessed many breaks with old traditions. The observational work of Purbach struck an altogether new note (Chapter XI), and to his pupil Regiomontanus fell the distinction of operating at Nürnberg the first European observatory of any consequence. The great Portuguese voyages of discovery provided new outlets for astronomical activity, and European mariners for the first time ventured across uncharted waters. Then came the Italian Renaissance and the first large-scale break with the imitative traditions of dogmatic scholasticism. Literature and art were the first to benefit, but the study of original Greek texts led to a new appraisal of ancient science and the philosophical ideas of Pythagoras and Plato.

The full scientific renaissance came later, but in the years of transition, and bridging the gap between the old and the new, stood the great work of Copernicus. This was the first independent challenge to the Ptolemaic system; appearances in the heavens, Copernicus argued, could be described equally well by supposing that the earth rotates, and like the other planets, revolves in a circular orbit about the central sun. Although Copernicus, like Ptolemy, viewed the solar system as a problem in geometry, he was not unaware of the physical implications of his change in viewpoint. As Chapter XII shows, many difficulties had to be surmounted before the heliocentric system gained widespread acceptance. Oddly enough the greatest contributions in its favour came from the accurate observational work of Tycho Brahe. Tycho rejected Copernicanism, yet his observations of the nova of 1572 and the comet of 1577 revealed great weaknesses in Aristotle's view of the cosmos. Furthermore, his systematic observations of the positions of the planet Mars enabled his disciple Kepler to discover the true geometrical relationship between the sun and the planets.

In the final chapter we see the end of most of the time-honoured ideas of the old astronomy. After the invention of the telescope, and quite apart from Kepler's geometrical discoveries, further evidence in favour of Copernicanism rapidly accumulated. Its final vindication is part of the story of modern astronomy, and I have therefore merely indicated the more important events in its subsequent progress. By about 1650, at any rate, the old notions of crystalline planetary spheres, combinations of circular orbits, uniform celestial motions, and the unchanging sphere of fixed stars had been consigned to the limbo of ancient myths. Astrology too was being hounded out of established science, but only to find a ready welcome from charlatans who traded (and continue to trade) on human credulity. It not only had nothing positive to contribute to the new astronomy, but also no place in the new reference framework of natural law.

To give the narrative a reasonable historical continuity I have purposely omitted accounts of Chinese and Hindu astronomy. While Oriental cultures made distinct and independent contributions to science, the fact remains that their theories and observations made over many centuries had but little effect on developments in the West. The main influencing factors, at least, are mentioned; reference is made to Hindu numerals, and to the Chinese inventions of the compass needle and spectacles. Nor should we overlook the value of early Chinese records which after about 700 B.C. give fairly reliable reports of eclipses, comets, shooting-star showers, and large naked-eye sunspots. Another omission is an account of European astronomy during the so-called Dark Ages, a period rich in astrology, magic, and folk-lore but quite sterile as regards astronomical observation. Even when the main stream of Graeco-Arabic scientific thought came to Western Europe, its assimilation and reduction monopolized the best efforts of many generations of scholars. Not until the fifteenth century did a few Europeans, more inquisitive than the rest, begin to observe the heavens on their own account.

Those already familiar with the early history of astronomy will readily appreciate that my story is based on a mere fraction of the wealth of available material. It makes no claim to be an original contribution to the subject, and is derived largely from second-hand sources. Any reader anxious to probe deeper should avail himself of some of the books listed in the Bibliography. Most of these are fairly accessible and contain references to papers of a specialist nature, and these in turn will enable him to trace any particular idea back to its original source. In any case, he should read forwards as well as backwards. My last chapter serves only to round off a glimpse of early ideas and ends at the stage where modern astronomy with its own particular richness and wonder begins.

H. C. K.

Slough, 1956

* CHAPTER I *

CELESTIAL DEITIES

*Take ye therefore good heed unto yourselves . . .
lest thou lift up thine eyes unto heaven, and when
thou seest the sun, and the moon, and the stars,
even all the host of heaven, shouldest be driven
to worship them, and serve them.*

Deuteronomy iv, 19

MAN'S interest in the sun, moon, and stars has been a long one, with beginnings lost in the mists of prehistory. Early man lived close to nature and was swayed by its unpredictable moods; invisible spiritual powers and agencies seemed alternately to prosper his plans and then to bring them to disaster. The phenomena of nature therefore became invested with human consciousness and personality. Such capricious and yet powerful influences had, at all events, to be conciliated and petitioned by either magic charms and incantations, or the worship of some representative totem or idol. In this way our early forefathers came to worship the things of the sky—the wind, rain, thunder, lightning, sun, moon, and the sky itself, for these powers seemed to rule all animate nature.

In normal seasons sunshine and rain induced unbounded fertility, yet the same influences could at other times produce droughts and floods. In some regions the effect of the sun on vegetative growth was evident enough. In others, water rather than sunshine seemed to be the mainspring of life, the real source of fertility. Through the action of occasional rainfall or flood-waters, an apparently sterile valley became carpeted with reeds, grasses, and flowers as if by magic. Removed from its influence, the transient pastures reverted to a barren waste. Water thus acquired a

9

sanctity for the first settlers in the Near East which we who live in almost over-watered lands can barely appreciate. As we shall see in detail presently, rain and water became attributable directly to the moon.

Nowhere was vegetative fertility more exuberant than in parts of the flat terrain of southern Mesopotamia, especially along the banks of the Tigris and Euphrates rivers. Settlers might exhaust the fertility of the land, but extensive floods from time to time deposited fresh layers of fertile silt on the wasted regions. Lagoons and marshy pools might shrink to puddles as the watercourses dwindled under the scorching heat of the summer sun, but these effects could be lessened through human intervention. Similar conditions existed in lower Egypt, except that one river, the Nile, refertilized the soil at its regular annual floodings. Settled agricultural communities arose in both places; they drained marshes, and by an intricate system of irrigation, regulated the floods and brought life-giving water to the rich alluvial soil away from the rivers' main courses. Hence the lush plain of Babylon called Edin, watered by tributaries and canals, and located where the two great rivers come to within thirty miles of each other, became a fitting scene for the temptation and fall of Man. Wheat, barley, millet, apples, and date-palms once grew in abundance on the plain, but the neglect of the waterways has now thrown the region into a barren waste.

In both Mesopotamia and Egypt, primitive peoples saw themselves involved in a great cycle of fertility, a cycle essentially dependent on water. Indeed, they supposed that the world had come into existence from a dark, primeval chaos of water, and that the moist mother element was the primary constituent of all things. In the course of time the birth, growth, and decay of plants and animals became related to the movements and appearances of the moon. Its monthly cycle of nearly thirty days from new moon to new moon provided a measure of time longer and no less reliable than the natural sequence of day and night. Its period coincided with the menstrual period of women—it was the bearer of seed,

the source of dew, dampness, life-giving moisture, and all pro-
creation. Its gradual waxing and waning from new moon to old
moon reflected within the compass of a month the longer life-
cycles on earth. Yet every month it appeared to die and to be
reborn, riding the night sky at full moon with undiminished brilliance. Hence it was regarded as a universal symbol for the renewal of life, a sign of generation and regeneration. Many tribes
hailed its monthly appearance with joy and thanksgiving, holding
a primitive watch-night service until the beating of drums and
cymbals told the glad news that the slender crescent was visible.
Small wonder, therefore, that in earliest times the moon often
took precedence over the sun in the hierarchy of gods, and was
generally worshipped as a living male deity.

One of the Semitic names of the moon was Sin, the name of the
Sumerio-Babylonian and Assyrian moon-god whose influence undoubtedly extended to Mount Sinai and beyond. In Chaldea the
moon was variously named Nammu, Sin, and Hur, and the moon-
god had his earthly sanctuary at Harran and the ancient capital of
Hur or Ur. As the favoured god of nomadic peoples who looked
to him for guidance and protection when they perforce travelled
at night, his influence seems to have spread far into Arabia and
Syria. Some writers have suggested that his worship continued
until well into the Christian era, especially in and around his sanctuary on Mount Sinai, sometimes called Mount Horeb. At Ur, at
least, Sin was referred to as being the 'lord of wisdom' and 'the
ordainer of the laws of heaven and earth'. A prayer of the time
says that his divinity 'like the far-off heaven, fills the wide sea with
fear'. He was given precedence over the sun in all early Babylonian
planetary tables, he had a sabbath or sacred day on every seventh
day, and Sivannu, the third of the twelve Babylonian months, was
dedicated to him.

In Egypt (and later in Greece under the name of Amon-Zeus),
Amon, the tribal ram-god of the Thebans, became a powerful
deity. His congress with the mother-goddess Mut produced
Khonsu, third member of the divine Theban trinity and the god

of the moon. Like the sun-god Ra, Khonsu was often portrayed as sitting in a boat, the aitist thereby intimating that the deity owed his motion, support, and nourishment to the mother element.

The Egyptians sometimes showed their god Thoth, originally an ibis totem, with a crescent or full disk on his head. Thoth, the moon, was the left eye of the sky-god Horus; Ra, the sun, was the right eye. The personification of wisdom, Thoth was the author of language and all learned works. He set the heavens in motion and thereafter counted the days, measured time, and invented mathematics and games of chance. He also kept records of the inundations of the Nile valley, since these were supposed to be under the influence of the moon. His most important function from the lay point of view was perhaps the weighing of the human heart against the feather of truth at the Last Judgement, an action which symbolized the final spiritual assessment of man.

Thoth was also the reputed author of many medical texts, and the Hermetic 'books' credited to him—thirty-two in number, and with six on medicine—were kept as reference books in the temples, but all are now lost. According to the Greeks, Imhotep, designer of the step pyramid at Sakkarah, was the first physician. Some two thousand years after his death he was deified and worshipped as a god of medicine, with temples at Memphis, Philae, and Thebes. Of his burial-place (once a shrine) and writings not a trace now remains. Great in his lifetime, but made far greater with the passage of centuries, Imhotep became associated with Thoth, and was finally equated by the Greeks with Asclepias, their own deity of healing.

In feminine rôle the moon appeared in Egyptian theocracy as Nit, the spinner and inventor of the loom. Weaving, however, was not necessarily a feminine occupation, for, as the historian Herodotus found in the fifth century B.C., the ancient Egyptians lived in a somewhat topsy-turvy woild. 'In Egypt,' he wrote, 'women go to market; men stay at the loom. Women carry loads on their shoulders, men on their heads. Their meals are eaten in the street; their "toilette" done indoors. Dough is mixed with the feet, mortar with the hands. And in writing or counting they work from right to left.'

In Syria, and especially with the Phoenicians, the cult of the mother-goddess Astarte (the Hebrew Ashtoreth), a divinity of maternity and fertility, seems to have had lunar associations. She derived from Enin-Ishtar, a lustful Sumerio-Babylonian goddess who was associated with the planet Venus. But Venus was not necessarily the only aspect in which Ashtoreth was recognized. Her name occurs several times in the Old Testament, for the erring Israelites were human enough to be attracted by the orgiastic rites and bacchanalian dances associated with her worship. Just as Baal, Bel, or Baalim was designated 'lord' and 'king' and had solar associations, so Ashtoreth in all probability represented the moon —the 'queen of heaven' referred to by the prophet Jeremiah.

Samuel persuaded the people to renounce polytheism, but the deep-rooted influence of Ashtoreth persisted until long after the reign of Solomon. Samuel records that when the Philistines came upon the body of Saul on Mount Gilboa, they stripped off the armour, which they carried into the temple of Ashtoreth as a trophy and thankoffering. Solomon is said to have lost his heart to numerous strange women, among them some Sidonian beauties who persuaded him to worship Ashtoreth and indulge in her dominant phallism. He made groves and erected altars in high places, but these were swept away many years later by Josiah, who temporarily purified Judah of polytheism. Josiah had the groves cut down and the sacred images ground to a dust which was 'strowed . . . upon the graves of them that had sacrificed unto them. And he burnt the bones of the priests upon their altars, and cleansed Judah and Jerusalem.' But an entire army of prophets operating over many years would not have arrested the cult of the Great Mother, Astarte-Ashtoreth. It not only persisted in Syria, but with various transformations spread far and wide over the Mediterranean, even reaching Britain.

The Hebrews adopted a year of twelve lunar months, and we

can imagine them on their housetops eagerly looking for the first appearance of the new moon, the herald of a new month. At times they may well have been led from the observation of the moon to its worship through Ashtoreth. Jeremiah once had occasion to complain that in the cities of Judah and streets of Jerusalem 'children gather wood, and the fathers kindle a fire, and the women knead their dough, to make cakes to the queen of heaven'. As will be seen later, similar cakes were offered to the goddess Hekate-Artemis of the Hellenes, a goddess who appears to have had lunar associations. Nor was the custom of making moon-cakes confined to ancient times. In a curious little book called *Moon Lore* published in 1885, the Rev. T. Harley writes that 'in a part of Lancashire, on the banks of the Ribble, there exists a precisely similar custom of making cakes in honour of the *Queen of Heaven*'.

Special objects, both animate and inanimate, have from time to time been dedicated to the moon. Ashtoreth and the Egyptian mother-goddess Hathor generally appeared with the head of a cow, and with a full or crescent moon perched between the horns. Thus the poet Milton's 'moonèd Ashtoreth, Heaven's queen and mother both' was at once a giver of moisture and a milk-giving cow. Again, and on a star map known as the Dendereh planisphere (see p. 25), the moon is represented by a female figure holding a small pig. When Herodotus visited Lower Egypt about 450 B.C. he found that it was customary to sacrifice pigs to the full moon on the eve of the festival of Osiris, a grain-god who had lunar aspects. Certain parts of these animals were burned, whilst the remainder was eaten sacramentally. Yet at any other time the Egyptians considered the pig unclean or taboo, and they would on no account eat its flesh. Poor people, unable to provide a real pig for sacrifice, made a model pig in dough. 'This', says Herodotus, 'they cook and offer in sacrifice, and so eat.' The practice, it seems, was analogous to the baking and eating of special moon-cakes.

Herodotus also commented on the mummies of cats preserved at Bubastis. These animals were probably dedicated to the moon, an association which their nocturnal habits and glistening eyes must have favoured. The Egyptians valued highly their domestic-ated, black, small-headed cats, and every endeavour was made to keep them within the kingdom. 'When a cat dies in a house,' Herodotus writes, 'its inmates shave their eyebrows; when a dog dies, they shave body and head all over.' On one occasion, and during the reign of one of the later Ptolemies, a Roman almost caused an insurrection by accidentally killing a cat. Bulls, rams, hawks, and crocodiles were also kept in the temples as sacred ani-mals, and were embalmed after undergoing a ritualistic death.

The snake or serpent, much feared and revered in ancient Egypt, had both solar and lunar associations. On the solar side the cobra (uraeus) was sacred to Ra, and its reared head in gold was the chosen symbol of royalty. The snake casts its slough as if reborn, it has a phallic shape, and it frequents pools and springs. It played an important part in foundation myths and human fer-tility rituals and was considered to be capable of healing, seducing women, and guarding sacred waters. Even among the constella-tions some figures are of a decidedly serpentine character, as for instance the Water Serpent (*Hydra*), the tortuous Dragon (*Draco*), and the fearsome Snake (*Serpens*) held by *Ophiuchus*.

According to an old Babylonian legend, Gilgamesh had the cherished plant of life snatched from him by a wily serpent. Legend also has it that a snake crept into the bed of Olympias during her husband's absence and thereby infused divinity into the future Alexander the Great. Another snake caused Alexan-der's downfall, for an old story says that whilst he was bathing in the Euphrates a water serpent removed an important talisman stone from his belt and spewed it into the river. Removed from the jewel's protective influence, Alexander was stricken with a fever which ended in his death. In an altogether different connec-tion, Moses is said to have transformed his magic wand into a ser-pent to impress Pharaoh, and during the journey across the wilderness he set up a serpent totem in brass. Those who had been bitten by snakes were healed as soon as they looked at the shining image. Until it was destroyed by King Hezekiah about 700 B.C., this totem was an important sacred symbol in the temple at Jerusalem. Also in a curative aspect an entwined snake appeared in Greek representations of their healer-god Asclepias, or Aesculapius to the Romans, and it also features in the emblem of the British Medical Association.

Metals and colours became associated with the heavenly bodies at a very early date. Gold and silver were dedicated to the sun and moon respectively, and their mixture, electrum, was supposed to have mystical properties. Temples to the moon were usually decked out in silver, the image of the moon-god being made entirely of that metal. The moon temples of ancient Peru contained vast plates of silver which bore the moon's effigy and simulated its pale, silvery light. Used in quite another capacity was moonstone, an opalescent to pearly mineral which was fashioned into amulets for promoting the health and fertility of the wearer. Another superstition, and one still current, is the belief that good luck will attend those who possess silver coins to turn over in their pockets when they first see a new moon.

The sun also was considered to be an elemental god, a living source of life, and sometimes the bright celestial home or representative of a beneficent god. Thus for the Greeks, Helios was the sun itself, whereas another Greek god, Apollo, resided temporarily in the sun. In like manner the old Vedic sun-god Vishnu of the Hindus represented the distant solar orb, whilst the sun-gods Savitar and Pushan respectively had moral and pastoral functions. Savitar, a wondrous all-seeing deity, daily cleansed the earth and dispensed moral wisdom. The more friendly Pushan, the 'Prosperer', guarded crops and live-stock and guided travellers on their ways.

The Babylonian sun-god Shamash, son of the moon-god Sin, was the second member of the old Sumerian trinity Sin, Shamash, and Ishtar. He personified the sun, and is generally portrayed as an old man with a long beard. Sometimes he carried a staff, sometimes a saw, using the latter to cut a gate in the eastern mountains and sending the dust like sunbeams to awaken mankind. Until a thoughtful priesthood provided him with a chariot drawn by two fiery mules, he made his long journey across the sky on foot. One cannot but feel kindly disposed to this bright old man who was initially obliged to make his unflagging and monotonous journey solely for the benefit of mankind.

Since the Egyptians were accustomed to travel along waterways, their sun-god Ra journeyed across the sky in great comfort in a celestial boat, accompanied by a choir and throng of adoring and administering deities. At sunset the boat reached the celestial river which was supposed to surround the disk-shaped earth, and which carried Ra and his travellers behind the mountains to the point of eastern ascent. Alternatively, the boat might travel to the east *via* the twelve chambers of the underworld.

The attributes of Shamash, like those of Thoth in Egypt, reached quite high ethical levels for the times. Shamash was the all-seeing sun, the mighty lord of judgement, the inventor of moral law, the avenger of crime, and the upholder of the rights of the weak. Hence when Hammurabi, the first king of united Babylon, drew up a famous code of laws nearly 4,000 years ago, he acknowledged that the laws originated from the sun-god. They were inscribed on a shaft or stela of diorite which is still preserved at the Louvre, but which was originally set up in the temple of Marduk in Babylon. Furthermore, they predate the Mosaic code by several centuries and are undoubtedly an extension of laws and precepts of an even earlier period. In practice, justice appears to have been unduly harsh, and quite simple offences were punished by physical maiming and disfigurement. The laws also covered professional duties, including medical practice. A suitably graded scale of charges covered all classes of patient, and severe penalties were imposed on those who broke the rules. A surgeon could, for instance, lose both hands if his patient lost an eye or died during an operation. In affairs of state, however, the god's protection and oracular pronouncements at high levels had a curiously selective bias towards the projects and wishes of the priesthood and the king or high priest. The former saw that temple-building and the flow of thankofferings reached fruitful levels, whilst the despotic warrior-kings of Assyria, under the blessings of Shamash and Marduk, embarked on crusades of destruction and merciless slaughter.

Over the course of many centuries the gods of ancient Egypt received several titles and different attributes, and the sun-god Ra was no exception. As Atum he had his genesis in the limitless depths of the primeval waters, Nu, being created by the divine artificer—the self-created Ptah. Ptah then made the waters Nu to separate into two parts: the waters above forming the heavens, and those below, the earth. In this ancient cosmology lies perhaps the germ of the Genesis story of the Creation, for there also the waters divided, and 'God called the firmament Heaven'. But whereas the sun made by God was a physical body only, the Egyptian Ra had two offspring—Shu, the god of air, and Tefnut, the lion-headed goddess of moisture. From this pair were born Nut, the sky-goddess, and Keb, the earth-god, and thence the famous national deities Osiris and Isis.

In very early times Ra's worship was centred at An, the Greek Heliopolis. Here the sacred Mnevis bulls were kept, and here Joseph, as vizier of Egypt, met and wedded the daughter of the high priest of Ra. Here also were numerous fine temples and obelisks, but after the third century B.C. many of the latter were transported to embellish the city of Alexandria. One of them, erroneously called 'Cleopatra's Needle', is now a familiar landmark on the Victoria Embankment, London. Another, one of two shipped to Rome when Augustus conquered Egypt, became the gnomon of an immense sundial. In Pliny's time, and owing perhaps to a tilt of the obelisk produced by an earthquake, the instrument was not particularly accurate. Heliopolis was also an important centre of sun-worship in the second century A.D., when the Emperor Antoninus Pius built a great temple there to Baal-Jupiter. The site is now a village suburb of Cairo, and the remaining obelisk and few mounds reveal nothing of the grandeur of the ancient city of the sun.

18

Ra was both the Egyptian word for the sun and the name of the sun-god. He was identified with Atum, an older divinity of the Upper Nile, and often assumed the form of Horus, the swift, hawk-headed god of Edfu. Sometimes he is portrayed as a disk with falcon's wings, sometimes as a human figure with the head of a hawk and carrying on his head a solar disk. Yet another form was Khepera, the sacred scarab beetle and emblem of the god who created the world afresh each morning. This beetle lays its eggs in dung, which it then rolls as a ball over the sand to a safe place of incubation. The Egyptians likened the ball to the solar disk, and probably noted the apparently spontaneous generation of the larvae from their lowly but nutrient medium. In the belief that they could absorb something of the power and strength of Khepera, the Egyptians wore scarab amulets, and even placed them hopefully about the bodies of their dead.

The sun-god also acquired different names and attributes according to his aspect in the sky. The great sphinx at Gizeh was dedicated to Ra Harmachis, or 'Horus at his rising and setting'.* Hernub, 'the golden Horus', manifested himself in the glory of the dawn, whilst the dying sun, Tum, was received in the sunset glow by Hathor, the cow-goddess of the western sky. In addition, it must be remembered that the pharaoh himself approximated to a god, assumed the title 'Son of the Sun', and claimed descent from Ra. At death, he became a god, a supreme celestial being, the very sun-god of the solar heaven.

An interesting and important development in Egyptian sun worship was the religion of Aten formulated and encouraged by Amenhetep IV in the fourteenth century B.C. Aten was the name of the solar disk, but Amenhetep's thoughts went beyond external appearances. He suggested that the dazzling Aten was the expression of a far greater power—a loving but formless Father who suffused all space and time. He changed his own name to Akhenaten, 'the blessed of the disk', and so developed his new idea that

* All the five then-known planets were 'Horuses' or falcon-headed male children of the sun-god.

he himself, his family, court, and followers, left the established polytheism of their fathers and wholeheartedly embraced monotheism.

To escape from the powerful priesthood of Amon at Thebes, the young King established Akhetaton, his own 'city of the horizon of Aten' at Tell-el-Amarna, about 160 miles up-river from where Cairo now stands. Here he spent his short life promulgating ideas of love, prayer, goodwill, and peace, whilst the prestige, military power, and financial resources of Egypt rapidly melted away. He died in the seventeenth year of his reign, leaving the country in a chaotic state, and with its enemies in full possession of the former Egyptian vassal state of Syria. Nor was he successful in establishing the new religion, for after his death the old gods headed by Amon-Ra returned, and the temples of Amon-Ra in particular were carried to even greater stages of splendour. Akhenaten was eventually branded as a heretic, and his name and figure were erased from temple walls and monuments. The beautiful palace at Akhetaton was dismantled, buildings were emptied of their treasures, and the city was allowed to fall into ruins.

In general, the gods of Egypt, and Lower Mesopotamia, were friendly to mankind—at least they were co-operative so long as their temples and priesthoods were adequately supported by tributes. Like Man, the gods grew tired and forgetful, they sometimes over-slept, they had human emotions and desires, and they had their enemies. Even Yahweh, the all-powerful God of the Israelites, having 'made heaven and earth, the sea, and all that in them is', had to rest on the seventh day, 'and was refreshed'. The priests of Babylon showed their consideration for a weary deity by placing an empty bed in the inner sanctuaries of their temples. Some gods, especially those of the Aztecs in Mexico, could be refreshed only by a large-scale shedding of human blood. For somewhat similar reasons, and also by way of appeasement, the Carthaginians are reputed to have sacrificed their offspring to a fiery Moloch or Baal. The custom of burning children persisted at Tophet, just outside Jerusalem, and Jeremiah laments the fact that the people of Jerusalem had 'built the high places of Tophet, which is in the valley of the son of Hinnom, to burn their sons and their daughters in the fire'. During the siege of Carthage by Aga-thocles, about 307 B.C., 200 boys from the best families are said to have been offered as burnt sacrifices to the planet Saturn. Yet per-haps the Carthaginians did not consecrate mass cruelty in this way —passing through fire may have been analogous to our practice of baptism with water.

An important theme in most religions is the struggle between good and evil, a conflict expressed in terms of the mutually hostile elements light and darkness. Strong dualisms of this kind are found in the Yang and Yin principles of Chinese naturism, in the two divine antagonists of ancient Persia, Adhura Mazda and Angra Mainyu, and in Marduk and Tiamat of Babylonian legend.

According to Egyptian mythology, Ra spent his youth fighting the powers of evil, the greatest of whom, Apepi, was always ready to attack him. Apepi personified the powers of primeval darkness, and was appropriately depicted in the form of a huge serpent or sometimes as an ox. Since the sun-god might meet him at any time on his journey through the underworld, Ra's navigators had to be constantly on the alert. In some temples special daily Apepi-frustrating services were held. Their proceedings doubtless pro-vided a lively spectacle whenever a partial or total eclipse oc-curred. Another myth tells how the weary Ra came to be hoisted aloft by the sky-goddess Nut. Nut turned herself into a cow, lifted Ra on to her back, and became the sky. To support Nut, Ra called in the assistance of Nut's husband Keb, the earth-god. Thus it transpired that the earth came to support 'the Lady of Heaven' in the guise of a heavenly cow to whose belly cling the twinkling stars and on whose back travels the solar bark. Alternatively, Nut is portrayed in female form, with her thin body arched over the earth and sprinkled with stars.

Since the priesthood had access to the inner thoughts of the gods on the one hand and the king on the other, it wielded considerable political and economic power. As the educated and privileged class it occupied a high social position, a position maintained by intermarriage and family inheritance. 'To each god there are many priests,' Herodotus writes, 'and of these one is called the high priest. When a priest dieth, his son taketh his office.' Since the gods demanded the first fruits, and plenty of them, the priesthood was kept busy ordering, regulating, and disposing of the holy traffic which coursed towards the great temples. It also regulated taxation, although itself immune from taxes, dictated the laws of marriage and real estate, and had time and opportunities for learned pursuits.

Yet Egyptian knowledge, like the Egyptian climate, had a decidedly static character. The necessary survey of landed property for the purposes of taxation, and the accurate re-fixing of boundaries washed away by periodical Nile floods, gave rise to no logical system of geometry. Despite the crystal-clear skies and the large number of priests concerned with the interpretation, recording, and later, the prediction of celestial events, Egyptian astronomy remained thin and non-progressive. The observation of the courses and changing positions of the sun, moon, and planets with reference to the canopy of stars continued for over forty centuries, yet no science of planetary motions resulted. Similarly, and in the rôle of embalmers, the surgeon-priests disembowelled hundreds of thousands of corpses and yet developed no system of anatomy. All these activities they appear to have carried no further than was necessary for their practical needs. The heavy hand of their religion, with its magic, superstition, elaborate ceremonials, and undue emphasis on the hereafter, effectively stifled rational thought.

Yet some astronomical science emerged from the temples, if only because the priesthood was responsible for the regulation of time. There were then no mechanical clocks or watches, and the 'time of day' or 'hour of night' had to be found from the sky. Hence the priests devised vertical sundials or 'gnomons', and water-clocks or 'clepsydrae', and made observations of the heavenly bodies with the 'merkhet'—a simple sighting device. In ancient times the gnomon was probably no more than a stick stuck vertically in the ground, thus forming a rudimentary sundial and the first astronomical instrument. In early Greece and late dynastic Egypt the gnomon rose like a slender obelisk from the centre of a graduated circular pavement. When the shadow of the pillar was at its shortest length on any one day, the gnomon indicated midday, for the sun was then at the highest point of its daily path in the sky. To obtain some idea of the time of the morning or afternoon, the observer noted the length and direction of the shadow.

An alternative shadow clock took the form of a portable L-shaped piece of wood, which in use was laid on its back in the direction of the sun. The shorter leg then served as a vertical gnomon and cast its shadow on graduations marked on the longer and horizontal leg. A complete early specimen of this 'clock' has yet to be found, but fragments and pictures suggest that it was in use about 1400 B.C. and probably at an even earlier date.

In the Egyptian version of the water-clock, a single vessel shaped like a flower-pot had a small hole near the bottom, and as the water level fell fairly steadily, uniform scales on the inner surface served as a linear clock face. There was, for instance, at Acanthae near Memphis, a perforated vessel of this type which it was the duty of 360 different priests to fill over the course of the religious year. The oldest specimen of an Egyptian water-clock dates from about 1400 B.C.

The Egyptians and Babylonians were both content to divide the day—the interval between sunrise and sunset—into twelve equal hours. Hence, except at the equinoxes, the hours of day were not equal in length to those of the night, and the lengths of both varied with the seasons. At the equinoxes, when the length of the day is equal to that of the night, these so-called *temporal* hours were equal to what the Greeks later called *equinoctial* hours. For the latitude of Athens, 38° N, they found that there were about sixteen equinoctial hours between sunrise and sunset at the

summer solstice and only eight at the winter solstice. The difference was only slightly less marked for central Babylonia, about
32° N, but the variations of temporal hours over the seasons apparently did not affect the simple Babylonian mode of life.

Even the invention of mechanical clocks about the fourteenth
century A.D. did not lead at once to our present system of equal
hours, and in Western Europe temporal hours survived until
clocks ceased to be expensive rarities. Indeed, it is more than
likely that in some parts of the East old customs and traditions still
continue to encourage the use of unequal hours.

For the priesthood and educated classes the time of night could
also be found by using the *dekanal* system, a kind of clock-
calendar of the stars, constellations and parts of constellations
based on a year of 360 days. A broad zone around the celestial
equator was divided into thirty-six equal groups or *dekans* (to use
the Greek term), the idea being that during the course of a lunar
year the thirty-six groups would successively rise in the east after
sunset at ten-day intervals or 'decades'. Realizing that 365 days is
a nearer approximation to the length of the solar year, the priests
prepared dekanal tables which allowed for the five extra days and
which were applicable for many years ahead. An observer could
therefore mark off ten-day intervals by noting the appearances of
successive dekans just above the horizon before sunrise. Alternatively, and knowing the calendar date, he could use the dekan
tables in conjunction with the observed disposition of the dekan
stars to find both the time and direction.

On star maps painted in tombs and funeral chambers, and often
on the insides of coffin lids, the constellations and dekans are
shown in a highly stylized and frequently debased form. Indeed,
these maps are hardly maps at all, but an assemblage of doubtless
sacred figures in human, half-human, and animal forms, accompanied by a few generally haphazardly placed stars. It is evident
that the ancient Egyptians originated their own constellation
figures at an early date; their groupings are mostly unlike those
used today. Coffin fragments found at Assyut, and about 4,000

years old, portray at least four constellation figures. Represented in outline are a scorpion goddess, a falcon (possibly our *Cygnus*, the Swan), a lion with stars arranged along his back and upper mane, and a complete bull with the *Pleiades* as the brush of his tail.

During Napoleon's campaign in Egypt, his scientific corps discovered a disk-shaped sky-map engraved on the red sandstone ceiling of the temple of Esneh at Dendereh. At the time it was thought that this planisphere was of great antiquity, but subsequent research proved that it dates only to 36 B.C., that is, to the time when Egypt was a Roman province. Nevertheless, subsequent finds elsewhere in Egypt, although of a much earlier period, show several of the figures depicted on the Dendereh planisphere. Its engraver was clearly interested in the figures and not in the relative star positions. Around the edge, and forming a separate system from the rest, are thirty-six dekan figures. The twelve signs of the zodiac* are all present, but they receive no extra prominence and have to be picked out one by one from the rest. Most investigators suggest that they are of Mesopotamian origin. Among them we notice that a pair of beam-scales (our *Libra*) replaces the claws of the Sumerian figure of the Scorpion, that the Bull (*Taurus*) has all his parts, and that the Crab (*Cancer*) is represented by a scarab beetle. The Lion (*Leo*) stands proudly in a boat outlined as a snake, and to his rear a human figure pulls his tail. The Virgin (*Virgo*) is small, but we recognize her by the ear of corn (the star *Spica* and a symbol of birth) which she carries in her left hand. Among the non-zodiacal figures are a large hippopotamus and a baboon. The familiar *Plough* of our times appears as the haunch of the ox, Apepi, and the Greater Dog (*Canis Major*) is shown as a recumbent cow with the star *Sirius* between its horns. Scattered among the figures of the zodiac are two large disks (the sun and moon) and five small figures in human form all carrying sceptres (the five planets).

---

* From the Greek Ζωδία (animals). The twelve divisions are: Aries, Taurus, Gemini, Cancer, Leo, Virgo, Libra, Scorpio, Sagittarius, Capricornus, Aquarius, and Pisces.

An earlier but differently arranged sky-map is the one painted on the ceiling of the tomb of Senmut, the chief architect to Queen Hatshepsut, who reigned about 1480 B.C. Over forty constellation figures, including the dekanal ones, are arranged in panels, but the few stars that are shown bear little to no resemblance to those in the sky. The *Pleiades* are represented by an egg-shaped figure, *Orion* is an upright male (Osiris), and *Sirius* appears as a crowned female deity (Isis).

Some investigators have inferred from the dimensions and precise orientation of the Great Pyramid or royal tomb of Khufu (Cheops) that its builders not only had a good knowledge of mathematics and astronomy, but that they were able to foretell many of the great events of the future. This opinion is quite unsupported and even negatived by the evidences of history and archaeology. The geometrical form of this massive but useless pile of masonry, and the remarkable accuracy with which the component blocks were made and fitted, reveal a knowledge of elementary geometry and the setting out of a right angle, but the edifice has no astronomical significance and enshrines no recondite mathematical principles. Like many other pyramids in the land of the pharaohs, its sides face the cardinal points—hence its builders knew how to determine a meridian. They knew also of the value of inclined plane, lever, and roller, for by these mechanical aids, coupled to the well-organized efforts of large gangs of slaves, over 5,000,000 tons of stone were brought over 400 miles and manœuvred into position. It is also pretty certain that when the overseers gazed back along its inclined entrance gallery at night they saw the star *Thuban*, the brightest star in the Dragon (α *Draconis*). From this we might infer that star observations were in progress about 3440 B.C., but historical evidence suggests that the Great Pyramid was built some 500 years later.

Owing to an effect known as *precession*, the celestial poles move in a complete circle round the poles of the ecliptic once every 25,800 years. At present the north celestial pole lies near *Polaris*, the bright star at the end of the tail of the Little Bear (α *Ursae*

Minoris). About 2800 B.C. it was near *Thuban*, whereas in 3440 B.C. *Thuban* was 3° 42′ below the pole—that is, the star was in the same direction as the inclined gallery. In this connection it is interesting to note that *Polaris* will be nearest the pole in A.D. 2102, whilst after another 12,000 years it will have given place to the bright star *Vega* of the Lyre (α *Lyrae*).

Certain Egyptian temples appear to have been so built that their main axes were in line with a particular bright star. As the chosen star rose above the horizon it shone along the axis of the building and could be seen from the sacred image in the sanctuary. Owing to precession, and after about 300 years, the original orientation had to be changed if the selected star or stars were still to be seen. This was done by either building a new temple or shifting the sanctuary sideways relative to the main entrance corridor. Other temples were orientated relative to the rising sun at the summer solstice. As the sun rose, its partial beams bathed the high priest or the gilded image of his god in a transfiguring glow. The solstitial orientation of the tall blocks of weathered granite at Stonehenge and Carnac (Brittany) apparently served a similar purpose in Neolithic times.

The Egyptians adopted a year of 360 days, or twelve lunar months of thirty days each, at a very early period. But by the fifth dynasty, about 3500 B.C. according to some historians, it was noticed that the seasons were arriving prematurely, and five extra intercalary days were added, making a year of 365 days. Other historians suggest that the adoption of a civil year of 365 days came much later, since the calendar in the *Ebers* papyrus, written about 1550 B.C., has a year of twelve months of thirty days each. The twelve equal months were retained, however, throughout Egyptian history, the five extra days being generally regarded as intruders into the year. They became known as 'the five days which are above the year', and were kept apart as special feast days; transactions undertaken during them received no legal status.

The Egyptian year began with the rise of the flood-waters of the Nile, since the river rather than the sun dictated the season of agricultural activity. In those days the river began to rise with fair regularity towards the end of June, at which time the *dog-days* or hot period began and the splendid dog-star *Sothis*, now called *Sirius*, rose in the east just before the sun. Once in possession of this knowledge, the priests could foretell when the flood would begin and when it would subside, and when the ground should be prepared and set with seed. Yet the seasons fit to a year of nearly 365¼ days, and relative to the civil year of 365 days the Egyptian Sothic calendar accordingly went astray one month every 121 years, or one year every 1,460 years. Hence in 238 B.C., in the ninth year of the reign of Ptolemy Euergetes, certain Egyptian priests met at Canopus on the Nile Delta and decreed the addition of one extra day once every four years. Their suggestion does not seem to have been generally welcomed, however, for when Augustus in 26 B.C. introduced the same idea at Alexandria, Egyptians elsewhere retained their old civil year of 365 days.

In Egypt, the river Nile and the star *Sirius* were regarded as different manifestations of Isis and her consort Osiris, the great grain-god of the dead. It is interesting to note that at a much later date the Persians also associated this star with water and growth. *Sirius* or *Tishtrya* was their rain-star and one of the so-called 'Royal Stars of Persia'. Through his own strength he routed Apaosha, the power of drought, and was favourably described as 'the white, shining, seen-afar, and piercing star'. He came from the golden east 'along the path made by the gods, along the way appointed for him' and gave the fields 'their fair share of the waters'.

In Greece, on the other hand, *Sirius* heralded midsummer drought, and its heliacal rising was associated with the advent of all manner of evil influences. 'The dog-star,' Virgil writes, 'that burning constellation, when he brings drought and disease on sickly mortals, rises and saddens the sky with inauspicious light.' To offset this scourge, physicians prescribed baths, cold drinks, and frequent rest periods in the shade.

CHAPTER II

THE STAR WORSHIPPERS

Each of the sixty great gods, my strong ones,
with his life will guide thee, Sin on thy right hand,
Shamash on thy left. . . . On mankind trust not;
bend thine eyes upon me; trust to me: I am Ishtar
of Arbela.

Assyrian cuneiform text

MUCH of our direct knowledge of the habits, beliefs, and customs of the ancient Egyptians has been gleaned from funerary papyri manuscripts and hieroglyphic inscriptions painted or engraved on coffins, monuments, and the walls of tombs. In Mesopotamia, on the other hand, the record is in cuneiform script. Wedge-shaped impressions were made with a stylus on clay tablets which were subsequently baked to brick hardness and stored for reference in libraries. In the majority of cases the impressions and consequent letters are extremely minute and indicate a high standard of vision on the part of both writer and reader; spectacles and magnifying glasses were unknown in those times.* Over the last century, archaeologists have unearthed and studied hundreds of thousands of more or less damaged sherds. Excavations at the site of Nineveh by Layard and Rassam in the nineteenth century alone produced over 25,000 pieces. These once belonged to the private library of the Assyrian king Assurbanipal and the library of the temple of Nebo, a god associated with the planet Mercury.

Many of the Ninevite tablets give calendars, astronomical calculations, and astrological reports, showing that the heavenly

---

* Layard discovered a slightly oval plano-convex lens of quartz in the ruins of Nimroud. The surfaces are poorly formed and it is unlikely that it was of much use as a visual aid. It is now in the British Museum.

bodies were being regularly studied in and before the seventh century B.C. Others retell old Sumerian stories of the creation, and the legend of Gilgamesh and his search for the Tree of Life. The Gilgamesh epic occupies twelve tablets, the eleventh of which aroused great interest when it was discovered by George Smith in 1872 to give a version of the Great Flood not unlike the Biblical account.

In the Assyrian story, Ea, lord of the deep, advises Ut-Napishtim to build a boat so that he and his household can escape from a watery death which the god Bel has in store for all living things. The family embark on the boat and for seven days torrential rains flood the land. The ship then grounds on the mountain Nisir, and Ut-Napishtim sends forth a dove and then a swallow, but both return. Later a raven is released, finds food, and does not return. The family thereupon leave the ship, set up incense vases, and pour out libations. 'The gods smelled a sweet savour', the tablet records. 'The gods gathered like flies over the sacrificer.'

In Babylonia the priests formed a class similar to its Egyptian counterpart. They were a sacerdotal caste, they kept their learning a closely-guarded secret, and they studied and worshipped the heavenly bodies in the belief that these controlled the destinies of men. In this sense they were astrologers, and it was from their astrology that the science of astronomy eventually grew. As we have already seen, Shamash was regarded as the symbol of law and order, whilst Sin served as a timekeeper and arbiter of many phases of human activity. Other wanderers against the background of stars are the planets, five of which were known from earliest times and related to separate deities. The sun, moon, and planets formed a divine society which was supposed to be intimately connected with events on the plains below.

Venus, the brightest planet, was associated with the goddess Enin or Ishtar, a deity who presided over both love and war. Her worship was centred mainly at Uruk, but she had temples at Nineveh, Uruk, Arbela, Merkes, and other centres. Although she was undoubtedly the principal goddess in the Babylonian pan-

theon, her qualities were not particularly lady-like. In the Gilgamesh epic she features both as a harlot and as a heroine—a
passionate and voluptuous creature full of contradictions. She was
at once chaste and lascivious, kind and cruel, cold and passionate
—as apt a compound of attributes of mother Nature as one could
wish to find in one personality. Cuneiform tablets tell of her great
part in a death and resurrection drama allied to the seasons and
agricultural growth. When her lover Tammuz died she went in
person to rescue him from the closely-guarded recesses of the
underworld. Deprived of her influence and of that of her lover,
the earth languished, the rites of love ceased, and all living things
began to die. Since the gods saw that they stood to lose all their
votaries, Ea sent a messenger to effect Ishtar's release. Tammuz
was awakened from the sleep of death, Ishtar received the water
of life, and life and reproductive energy returned to the earth.
Thus the planet Venus, in common with the moon, symbolized
regeneration and resurrection, and in the form of Ishtar represented a love that could defy all terrors and 'go to the ends of the
earth' to achieve its purpose.

It is remarkable how the ingredients of the Ishtar–Tammuz
myth found expression in stories at other places and in other
times. The Isis–Horus myth which symbolized the renewal of the
seasons was celebrated all over Egypt by 1e-enactments of the
main theme accompanied by dirges and the strange sound of the
sistrum. In an ancient Hittite myth, the god of vegetation, Tele-
pinush, leaves his country. Life begins to perish, but a bee sets out
to find him and succeeds in bringing him and life back to the
stricken earth. Again, and at a much later date, the Greeks told
how Persephone is carried away to the underworld while she
gathers flowers in the meadows. Her sorrowing mother Demeter
thereupon roams the earth seeking her child, and life on the
earth begins to languish. Then there is the story of Orpheus's
visit to the underworld to recover his beloved Euridike, killed by
a snake-bite. While it is too much to say that these and similar
Celtic and Teutonic stories have a common origin, there is no

doubt as to their connection with ideas of fertility and seasonal growth.

The planet Venus revolves about the sun in an orbit smaller than that of the earth and in a period relative to the earth of nearly 584 days. Hence Venus appears alternately as a morning and evening star, and never recedes further from the sun than about 48°, the value of its *maximum elongation* as it is called. The Babylonians, of course, had no idea of planetary motions about the sun, and having no telescopes they were quite unaware that the planet goes through phases analogous to those of the moon. They realized, however, that Venus is both the 'white-winged forerunner of the sun' and the star in the west, an association which Greeks in the fifth century B.C. hailed as a new discovery. They also noted on their clay tablets the times of the planet's disappearance and reappearance in both the east and west, that is, before the sun rose and after it had set.

As an evening star Ishtar was a goddess of love and patroness of fertility and was often portrayed as a dove. As a lover she bestowed her favours on Akki, a humble irrigator who was supposed to be responsible for rearing Sargon I of the third millennium B.C. This son of an unknown mother was found floating on the Euphrates in a basket of reeds sealed with pitch. Akki raised the foundling, and later Ishtar guided his steps to the throne. As a morning star she was a goddess of war, a 'summoner of armies' and one 'strong in battle'. In this dread capacity she rained fire upon hostile lands and caused the earth and heavens to tremble.

Ishtar was a favourite with the Assyrians, and especially with the great kings Sennacherib, Esarhaddon, and Assurbanipal of the eighth and seventh centuries. As Ishtar of Arbela, 'the city of four gods', she is made to say to Esarhaddon: 'By thy side I go, fear not. . . . Thine enemy, like the harvest gathering of the month of Sivan, before thy feet descends to do battle. The Great Lady am I. . . . Thine enemy I cut off and I give to thee. . . . Fear not, O Esarhaddon. . . . I will ease thy heart. . . . Respect as for thy mother thou hast caused to be shown to me.' And at a later date, when Assurbanipal sought her counsel before going to war, a priest dreamt that 'Ishtar who dwells in Arbela came unto me begirt right and left with flames, holding her bow in her hand and riding in her open chariot as if going to battle. . . . Thy heart's desire shall be accomplished. Thy face shall not grow pale with fear. Thy feet shall not be arrested: thou shalt not even scratch thy skin in the battle. In her benevolence she defends thee, and she is wroth with all thy foes. Before her a fire is blown fiercely to destroy thy enemies.'

Of the other planets, Mercury was associated with Nabu, a god of wisdom similar to the Egyptian Thoth. His image was sometimes shown with four wings—an indication that he moved rapidly in the sky. Mars, with its fiery colour, was associated with Nergal, a god of war, fever, and plague, Jupiter with Marduk, the chief god of united Babylon and a deity with solar attributes, and Saturn with Nibib or Adar.

The importance attached to three of these deities and to the practice of astrology is seen in the following translation from one of Assurbanipal's cuneiform texts: 'Marduk, master of the gods, granted me as a gift a receptive mind and ample power of thought. Nabu, the universal scribe, made me a present of his wisdom. Ninurta and Nergal endowed my body with strength, vigour, and unrivalled power. The art of Master Adapa I learned, the hidden treasure of all scribal knowledge, the signs of heaven and earth . . . I have studied the heavens with the learned masters of oil divination, I have solved the laborious problems of division and multiplication, which were not clear, I have read the artistic script of Sumer and the dark Akkadian, which is hard to master. . . .'

Mars or Nergal was a fearsome deity, since he brought both victory and defeat. He was regarded as being the most perfect of all warriors, the most violent of the gods; his star shone with 'awe-inspiring splendour'. Marduk was originally the local god of Babylon, and after the reign of Hammurabi, when that city became greater than all others, he rose to become the leader of the entire celestial pantheon. Although he received associations with the planet Jupiter, he gradually usurped the power and qualifications of Shamash, and had his festivals fixed according to the equinoxes. He it was who fought the dragon of chaos, Tiamat, and, slitting her open like a shellfish, made one part the heavens and the other the earth. As a god with solar interests he later appears to have been identified with Bel, Baal, Baalzebub, and Merodach, the sworn enemies of the Hebrew prophets.

Since the flat plains of Mesopotamia provide no natural heights, the temples and 'high-Places' of important deities were built on the summits of immense staged towers or ziggurats. Every great city possessed at least one ziggurat, each structure being orientated with its angles aligned on the cardinal points of the compass and conceived as a kind of Jacob's ladder by which man might mount to heaven and commune direct with the gods. The remains of the great ziggurat dedicated to the god Marduk still rise some 140 feet above the rubble of Babylon. Its predecessor, the Tower of Babel, mentioned in the Bible as the scene of the confusion of tongues, no doubt stood on the same site. By the seventh century the old and perhaps original tower had fallen into grave disrepair, especially since 689 B.C. when the Assyrian king, Sennacherib, tried to annihilate Babylon. King Nabopolassar therefore decided to rebuild it so that its pinnacle might again 'strain upwards to the skies'. By the time it was completed by his son Nebuchadnezzar, the new ziggurat rivalled all others in size and splendour.

Built on a platform 288 feet square, the Marduk ziggurat rose in a series of seven immense stages above the large surrounding courtyards and associated temples to a height of some 250 feet. Building-stone was scarce in southern Mesopotamia, hence the central core was composed of sun-dried bricks cemented together with pitch. These straw-bonded clay bricks weathered rapidly, but the exterior of the tower was rendered more durable by using baked bricks and more colourful by glazing their outside surfaces. Each stage was smaller and of a different colour from the one immediately below, and was dedicated to one of the divinities associated with the sun, moon, and five known planets. An exterior stairway reached like a great buttress to the first three terraces, after which closely-guarded interior flights led to the topmost platform and the surrounding shrine of Marduk, itself 48 feet high. Herodotus saw this shrine and noted the deep-blue glazed brickwork and the handsome interior furnishings. A richly-covered divan and a gilded table were ready for the god whenever he felt tired, while a favoured maiden awaited a ritual copulation with the god which, it was believed, would renew the fertility of the land.

Another great ziggurat, dedicated to Nabu, was built at Borsippa, some fifteen miles south-west of Babylon. This likewise was erected on a brick-encased platform, and rose in seven stages to a total height of some 250 feet.

Abraham was born at Ur on the Euphrates about 2000 B.C., and therefore saw its massive three-staged ziggurat, which was dedicated to the moon-god Sin. In his time the tower was about 100 years old, having been built between 2106 and 2123 B.C. by King Ur-Nammu. Perhaps as a young man Abraham marvelled at its vast proportions and saw the great procession of priests in all its barbaric splendour as it slowly wended up one of the three broad stairways which led to the lower terrace. The Roman Jew, Josephus, says that Abraham disputed with the priesthood and told it that if the heavenly bodies were deities of any consequence they would move more regularly in the sky. The fact that they did not he ascribed to their subservience to a greater God. 'For which doctrines,' Josephus records, 'when the Chaldeans and other people of Mesopotamia raised a tumult against him, he thought fit to leave that country.' The story may not be true, but it is at least a good one and not at all improbable.

The ziggurat at Ur still raises its lower stages some 70 feet above the formless plain, but only because the Joint Expedition under C. L. Woolley in the 1920s removed some thousands of tons of piled-up rubbish. Like other ziggurats, it was at once a temple and an observatory, and from the military viewpoint must have been an excellent watch-tower. From its topmost platform and upper terraces the priests surveyed an immense horizon, and in the tranquillity of the night felt that they were at one with the denizens of the star-spangled sky.

Seen from the sun, the planets all move regularly in one direction across the solar sky. Seen from the earth, and owing to the motion of the earth and its position in the solar system, the planets appear to describe orderly but complicated paths against the background of stars. Mercury and Venus, for instance, both oscillate to and fro about the sun and keep it company, in that they appear in its neighbourhood. The major planets, that is, those planets outside the orbit of the earth, often appear in parts of the sky opposite to the position of the sun. Sometimes they move backwards instead of forwards, and at the end of such *retrogressions* appear stationary relative to the stars. Nevertheless they all keep within a narrow zone on either side of the apparent annual path of the sun (the ecliptic), owing to the fact that their orbits about the sun all lie nearly in the plane of the earth's orbit. Persistent observation shows that each planet appears to move round the heavens in a constant period, also that at times of *conjunction* two planets and perhaps more gather together in the same section of the zodiac. In 1019 B.C., for instance, the ancient Chinese recorded that all five planets gathered near 'Fang', the star group, β, δ, and π *Scorpii*.

The movements and relative dispositions of the planets, also the risings and settings, disappearances and returns of Venus and Mars in particular, received great attention. One recovered cuneiform tablet gives observations of the appearances of Venus over a period of twenty-one years and dates back to about 1900 B.C. or even earlier. It was certainly known at this time that Venus made five circlings in eight years, or, as we would say today, that five synodical years of Venus almost equal 2,920 days. As observations accumulated, so further regularities became evident. Jupiter was found to require twelve years to travel round the sky, whilst Saturn required as long as twenty-nine years. Eclipses of the sun and moon were recorded, and by about the fourth century B.C. it was discovered that eclipses which occur during a cycle of 223 lunations, or eighteen years eleven months approximately, repeat themselves in the following cycle. Although visible from other parts of the world, many of the solar eclipses of this cycle (called the *Saros*) were not visible from Babylonia during cycle repetitions—which fact makes its discovery all the more praiseworthy. Once in possession of these and other regularities, the Chaldeans or astrologer-priests of later Babylonia were able to make quite good predictions of astronomical events.

A knowledge of Babylonian eclipse records later passed into the Greek world, and Ptolemy for one made use of the eclipses of 721 and 720 B.C. to test the accuracy of his tables of the motions of the sun and moon. In recent times also, and at the hands of the late J. K. Fotheringham, these early eclipse records enabled the determination of the slight increase in the earth's period of axial rotation—an increase assessed at the rate of about one thousandth of a second per century.

As early as 2900 B.C., and perhaps even earlier, the Sumerians grouped the stars into constellations which were, to some extent, somewhat similar to those used today. Thus we find mention of the Twins (*Gemini*), the Scorpion (*Scorpio*), the Little Horse (*Equuleus*), the Sea Snake (*Hydra*), the Raven (*Corvus*), and the Eagle (*Aquila*)—although these are of course all called by Babylonian names synonymous with their Greek equivalents. Some of the figures also appear on Babylonian boundary stones of the period 1100 B.C.; two interesting examples are the zodiacal constellations of *Capricornus*, a goat with the tail of a fish, and *Sagittarius*, a centaur carrying a fully-drawn bow. There seems little doubt that the Chaldeans used twelve zodiacal signs and that these were nearly all similar to the familiar figures of today. They knew for certain that these twelve signs cover the ecliptic zone frequented by the sun, moon, and planets. Less certain is whether they divided this zodiacal zone into twelve *equal* parts; this important step appears to have been taken very much later in astronomical history. Some writers, however, have been tempted to seek the twelve zodiacal constellations in the twelve incidents of the Gilgamesh epic. We read there how the hero slew the Bull, how he scorned the persistent amours of Ishtar (a female divinity, howbeit no Virgin), and had adventures with two Scorpion men. The watery theme in the Deluge story perhaps ties up with the Water-carrier (*Aquarius*). Again, the discovery of a list of ancient Babylonian month-names refers to a Bull, Ishtar, and 'The Curse of Rain' in separate months. The other names, it must be frankly admitted, bear no resemblance to the other zodiacal signs, and the comparison seems a highly forced one. It should also be mentioned that although the Babylonians used a dekanal system, it had nothing to do with the zodiacal zone, but operated around the celestial equator.

Like the early Egyptians, the Sumerians and Babylonians at first adopted a year of 360 days. Their calendar operated on a monthly basis, but as the lunar month is about twenty-nine and a half days and not thirty days, twelve lunar months do not equal the solar year of $365\frac{1}{4}$ days. Since they fall short of it by about eleven days, an additional thirteenth month had to be intercalated once every two to three years. The first day of the month began with the first appearance of the new moon in the glow of the western sky—hence the days were reckoned from evening to evening. The Hebrews, among others, used the same basis, hence the words in *Genesis* to the effect that 'the evening and the morning were the first day'.

When the Babylonians introduced the quite arbitrary idea of the week, they always made the first day of each month the first day of the week. Every seventh day was sacred to Sin, and a day on which chariot-riding and the eating of cooked flesh were considered taboo. The seven days, however, did not become identified with the sun, moon, and planets until about the first century B.C. A luni-solar year of 365 days entered into the calendar on the first year of the reign of Nabonassar, that is, in 747 B.C., and with it came a more reliable chronology. After this year the Babylonians maintained a continuous dated record of observations.

Just as we today use a system of numeration based on the numbers ten and twelve, so the Babylonians for no apparent reason based their arithmetic on the number sixty. This led to the division of the circle into 360 equal parts or degrees, and along with the hour, the further subdivision into sexagesimal minutes and seconds. Angular distances between stars were measured in units of the *ell*, which had a value of about two degrees, and each *ell* was divided into twenty-four *dactyli* or fingers. Several Greek astronomers, including Hipparchus of the second century B.C., employed these units. In Babylonia, and after about the sixth century B.C., some form of graduated sighting instrument seems to have been regularly used, and its improvement over the next three centuries gave rise to observations of increasing accuracy. Through the development of the beam balance, moreover, small quantities of water from a clepsydra could be weighed with great accuracy, the weights being interpreted in minutes and even seconds of time. In public life, however, minutes of time had little practical significance until well after the introduction of mechanical clocks in the thirteenth century A.D. Even in Tycho Brahe's observatory at Hveen in the sixteenth century, balance clocks were found so unreliable that Tycho experimented with mercury clepsydrae in an attempt to measure small intervals of time.

Babylonian astronomy never freed itself from the claims of astrology. Even in the later Seleucid period, when the priesthood was stripped of its material power and influence, observations appear to have been dedicated to one or another of the celestial divinities. There was always a solid core of divination and astrological practice, always the search for omens and the belief that the destinies of men are written in the stars. Just as Egypt had its magicians and Israel its prophets, so Babylonia had its diviners who saw omens in the most trifling series of events. The observers who patiently drew up complex planetary tables probably pondered over the interpretation of dreams, the flight of birds, the behaviour of drops of oil on water, and the appearance of the livers * of sacrificed sheep.

* The liver was supposed to be the seat of life.

About 562 B.C., when Nebuchadnezzar dreamt strange dreams and sensed impending disaster, he 'commanded to call the magicians, and the astrologers, and the sorcerers, and the Chaldeans, for to show the king his dreams'. Daniel alone could interpret them satisfactorily. Later, when Isaiah predicted the destruction of 'the harlot Babylon' at the hands of Cyrus, king of Persia, he poured scorn on her traditions. 'Thou art wearied in the multitude of thy counsels. Let now the astrologers, the stargazers, the monthly prognosticators, stand up, and save thee from those things that shall come upon thee.'

Despite Isaiah's dread prediction, the Persians under Gobryas did not sack Babylon in 539 B.C., although the royal monarch Nabonidus was burned to death during the storming of the royal citadel. In other quarters, and especially among the Jews in captivity and the priesthood, the Persians were received more as deliverers than conquerors. Nabonidus had introduced foreign gods into the temples, and when Cyrus restored the local deities to their shrines, the activities of astrologers, stargazers, and sorcerers took on a new lease of life.

Nineveh had already fallen. Assurbanipal's preoccupation with learned pursuits perhaps accounted for the weakening of his empire, although when he made war he did so with wanton savagery. The fact remains that when he died in 626 B.C. its resources and military strength were at a low ebb. Twelve years later the united Median and Babylonian forces began a two-year siege of Nineveh, and when in 612 the defences finally fell, the city suffered great devastation. Palaces and temples were reduced to rubble, and Assurbanipal's library became buried under fallen walls. The invaders also destroyed the extensive irrigation system built by Sennacherib, so that both the commercial and the agricultural life of the district collapsed. From Roman times and until the nineteenth century, Nineveh was a sand-covered mound in a desert of sand.

Babylon suffered further damage when the Persian king Xerxes tried to level out the great ziggurat to Marduk. Persian influence ceased after 331 B.C., when at Gaugamela, about 50 miles north-west of Arbela on the upper Tigris, Alexander routed the immense forces of Darius. The Macedonian took possession of Babylon and saw something of its former splendour, but by then many of the city's great buildings were in ruins. Impressed by the size of the mound of bricks which represented the former Marduk ziggurat, Alexander is said to have had his army spend some 600,000 work-days in ineffectual attempts to clear away the debris. As a result of Macedonian occupation a few new buildings in the Greek style replaced some of the ruins, but Babylon never became a popular Greek colony. The latest information regarding the continuance of worship to Babylon's gods relates to 29 B.C., when in a corner of the city Marduk and Baal were worshipped as a two-fold deity under the name of Anna-Bel or 'Heavenly King'.

After Alexander's death in 323 B.C. and the second partition of the Macedonian empire, Babylonia and Syria passed to the Seleucids. The dynasty ruled from 312 to 147 B.C., after which the Parthian Arsacids took over until the third century A.D. The first ruler, Seleucid Nicator, persevered in carrying out Alexander's dream for the Hellenization of Babylonia, to which end he founded several Greek colonies and retained the Greek way of life. But while Babylon was being used as a brick quarry for the building of the new city of Seleucia, old traditions lingered on in the secondary towns. At Borsippa and Sippara, for instance, and to mention only two sites which have as yet revealed something of their rich past to modern archaeologists, astronomical observations continued with vigour and were even developed to higher stages.

By this later period, that is, around 300 to 200 B.C., the use of water-clocks, sighting devices, and perhaps even graduated instruments had revealed more complex periodicities in the motions of the planets. By equally complex arithmetic operations, these movements were represented by sequences of numbers written in sexagesimal notation and arranged in tabular form on clay tablets. The study of these tablets, or better, shattered fragments, makes it clear that Chaldean astronomers of the schools of Kidinnu and

Naburiannu (called respectively Cidenas and Naburiannos by later Roman authors) were not only measuring the distances of the planets from prominent stars (as was done since the sixth century B.C.), but recording their positions in the zodiac in degrees, minutes, and seconds of arc. From their tables they could read off the periods of the planets and predict their positions and daily movements; they could tell when a planet would be visible or invisible, and when it would advance, become stationary, or retrogress. Yet the same tables enshrine no knowledge of circular orbits in space. 'For the Chaldean astronomers,' A. Pannekoek writes,* 'the planets remained, manifestly, up to the last centuries, divine luminaries roaming along the heavenly vault, proceeding and returning, in pendulations and loops; orbits in space are never heard of, save occasionally as an echo of rumours of Greek origin.'

* In *Popular Astronomy*, 55, 427, 1947.

CHAPTER III

GODS, SCALES, AND SOULS

*Many glorious sights there are of the courses in
the heavens traversed by the race of blessed gods,
as each goes about his own business; and whoso-
ever wills, and is able, follows, for envy has no
place among the Heavenly Choir....*

Plato

COMPARABLE in antiquity to the early Babylonians was the
Minoan civilization which arose around the Aegean Sea and which
had its centre at Knossos on the island of Crete. Archaeological
and historical research makes it clear that as early as 2500 B.C., and
perhaps even earlier, this civilization had a well-developed island
culture and religion altogether different from those of Egypt and
Mesopotamia. The Minoans had contacts with the peoples of
Egypt and the Syrian coast; they also established colonies on the
western shores of Asia Minor. On the mainland of Greece they
established high cultures at Mycenae, Argos, and Sparta, but about
1200 B.C. these were absorbed by new masters called the Achaeans.
A century later all succumbed to barbaric invaders from the north
—the Dorians. They swept down the Greek peninsula to the
Peloponnesus and even reached Crete itself. Refugees streamed
eastwards, among them the Ionians, one of the pre-Dorian mainland peoples who settled on the western coast and islands of Asia
Minor. By the seventh century B.C. these mixed races had acquired
some sense of cultural unity, despite the rivalry and mistrust
which grew up between individual city states. The Greeks, or as
they called themselves, Hellenes, thus overspread the peninsula,
the islands of the Aegean, an extensive part of the coastline of

Asia Minor, and eventually, the coasts of Sicily, Libya, southern Italy, and southern France.

One result of this cultural union of peoples was the production of a religion which combined at least three dominant and distinctive traits. From ancient Crete and Mycenae came traditions associated with the mother-goddess and a group of feminine deities who presided over earth, water, and fertility. From the north and Syria came strains of semi-oriental and barbaric nature cults and their associated orgiastic ceremonies. From the war-stricken mainland came stories of Achaean heroes and heroines who fought, revelled, and loved with barbaric abandon. The story of their exploits was told about 900 B.C. in the great epic poems attributed to Homer. In the *Iliad* and *Odyssey* we find painted the classic lineaments of an entire pantheon. Headed by the exalted Zeus, an idealization of a human father, the immortal gods lived above the snowy heights of Mount Olympus in northern Thessaly, and made the broad expanse of heaven their playground. They sported with nature, hurled thunder and lightning across the sky, practised free love, and were generally so busy with their own affairs that they descended to assist mortals only in times of national emergency.

A fourth but much later influence, judicial astrology,* came direct from Babylon. The doubtful honour of having introduced it to the Greek mainland is generally accorded to Berosus of the fourth to third century B.C. He was originally a priest of Bel-Marduk at Babylon, left that city after its seizure by Alexander, journeyed to Egypt along the Macedonian supply route, and crossed to the island of Cos in the Aegean. At Cos he wrote a history of the Chaldeans, a work now lost, but fragments are preserved in the writings of Josephus and other early historians.

Berosus taught both astrology and astronomy, and at Cos he probably came into contact with the celebrated medical school established about 430 B.C. by Hippocrates. If so, his ideas must have appeared strange to the physicians who practised there. Hip-

* As distinct from 'horoscopic' astrology and the study of nativities.

pocrates and his immediate disciples had broken away from the hitherto mystical interpretation of disease. Instead, they sought natural causes, studied the patient and his environment, and endeavoured to be accurate in observation and careful in prognosis. To them, disease no longer ranked as an infestation of devils or punishment sent by the gods, but rather as a condition caused perhaps by a change in food, climate, or occupation. Of epilepsy Hippocrates writes: 'As for this disease called divine, surely it has its nature and causes which can be found by those who seek them.' He also taught that the physician should work hand-in-glove with nature rather than interfere with its operations. Drugs were therefore largely replaced by baths, special barley and honey diets, and hot fomentations.

If these ideas seemed strange to contemporaneous Greeks, they must have been revolutionary to one with Berosus's background. What effect his astrology had on Hippocratic teaching we shall never know. He left Cos for Athens, where, among other then strange doctrines, he taught that the moon is a sphere, half of which shines by its own light.

Berosus was not the only Chaldean to bring new ideas to Greece, for the downfall of the Persian empire probably encouraged many other priests to do likewise. Long before the Macedonian conquest, Greek traders had settled at Naucratis and Daphnae in the Nile Delta, and there is every reason to believe that from the late seventh century B.C. a frequent if somewhat thin interchange of ideas accompanied the active trade relations between the near Orient and the Aegean. After the middle of the sixth century B.C., Persian influence extended throughout Asia Minor, and many Greeks went as envoys to the Persian court or joined Persian armies as mercenaries. But the full impact of oriental ideas came after the Macedonian conquest, for although Alexander set up Greek colonies in the orient and took Hellenism deep into India, Asia in return came to influence Greek culture.

Until the fourth century B.C. the Greek religion was a kind of open-air pantheism—a heterogeneous mixture of rural gods, rustic nymphs and spirits, and local heroes. It was essentially a religion of humanism, a man-made affair so founded on ancestor-worship and infused into art and literature that it at once needed no prophets and occasioned no blasphemies. There was therefore no single purpose or centralized national religion, no more than there was at any time a single national culture shared by all Greeks. No sacred book set forth moral laws or painted right and wrong in sharply contrasting colours. To do right in the eyes of his compatriots, the Greek had only to show respect to the deities of his own city-state by performing the prescribed ceremonies correctly, and by participating in public festivals of thanksgiving. To despise or question the ethical value of the gods was a crime punishable by death, or fine and banishment. On the other hand, no fault was found with intellectuals like Plato and Xenophanes, to mention only two, when they inclined towards monotheism, for the Greek was free to worship any sort or kind of deity, and even none at all. Yet both were censured as soon as they questioned the ethical value of the Olympian pantheon.

In such a loose system the priesthood, unlike that in Egypt and Mesopotamia, occupied a subordinate position. It might at times impress its ideas through complex rituals, mystic rites, and oracles like those at Delphi, Delos, Eleusis, and Olympia, but it exercised no permanent control. The clashes between the priesthood, the state, and the representatives of science and philosophy which became all too frequent in later ages were happily absent in ancient Greece.

While the Greeks considered that only barbarians worshipped the heavenly bodies, they were not averse to paying homage to deities with astronomical attributes. Never very dominant at the outset, these attributes gradually gave ground over the years to others of a more direct and homely nature. Hence the Greek religion had no dependence on stargazing, nor did it require the continuance of Chaldean astrology. Instead, it borrowed the least productive aspect of the latter—the mystical mumbo-jumbo of divination and its consequent oracular delusions.

Homer called Zeus the 'Cloud-Gatherer' and made him a god of the sky and weather, a divinity who has rain, thunder, and lightning to hand. Such mastery over the elements of the sky invested him with great power—he was the sky-god *par excellence*. He was a fervent lover, and his one legitimate wife, the only really married goddess on Olympus, was the 'ox-eyed' and shrewish Hera, who presided over marriage and childbirth. From her ample breasts the Milky Way was formed, and in this aspect it is interesting to note that the Arabians later regarded this zone as 'the mother of the heavens' who feeds the stars with her milk. Although Hera had lunar attributes, these were far more evident in Artemis of Ephesus, whose cult flourished in Asia Minor long before the Greeks settled there. Besides being candidly portrayed as a goddess of fertility, Artemis appears also as a protector of the young and as a sender of plagues and death to men. Like Ishtar of olden times, she thus played a dual rôle, and her image in the great temple at Ephesus was exuberantly adorned with multiple breasts,* whilst the legs were shrouded in grave-clothes. As a moon-goddess she appeared more decorously, for she wore a long robe and crescent diadem, and carried a torch. As a goddess of the chase she is portrayed with a spear or variously with a bow, quiver, and arrows. Under the Romans she became Diana, the 'great goddess Diana' of the *Acts of the Apostles* 'whom all Asia and the world worshippeth'.

Selene or Mene, the moon itself, is of little importance in Greek mythology. She loved Endymion, a beautiful shepherd-boy of Mount Latmos, who, either at his own request or through the contriving of Selene, was cast into perpetual sleep. In Roman times the moon was called Luna, and both Livy and Tacitus refer to temples dedicated to her worship.

Some mythologists consider that the mysterious triple-headed divinity Hecate also had lunar associations. As a goddess of the underworld she is said to have been Proserpine, the formidable

---

* Likewise an attribute of Ishtar, whose eyebrows also were sometimes grotesquely multiplied.

queen of the equally terrible Hades, the ruler of the souls of the dead. As a goddess of the earth she was, like Artemis, concerned with fertility. As a goddess of the sky she was identified with Selene, and in her triple aspect perhaps represented three phases of both the moon and womanhood. The new moon was likened to girlhood, the full moon to maturity, and the old moon to decrepitude. She was also a goddess of the crossroads, and perhaps her triple aspect was designed to enable her to look down three roads at once. Crossroads were generally regarded as scenes of ghostly activity, and we are told that housewives used to assemble there on the night after full moon and offer barley cakes to Hekate-Artemis. The cakes held candles, which it was thought would replenish the moon's light and so help it to dispel the darkness of night. Moon-cakes were also made in ancient China on the occasion of special annual festivals held every eighth month.

The original Greek sun-god was Helios, but after about the fifth century B.C. he became identified with Apollo. Helios (Roman *Sol*) was then reserved more for the name of the physical sun than for an important solar deity, and as such became the celestial residence of Apollo. As a sun-god, Helios rose every morning from his watery bed in the Homeric river Oceanus. Ascending like Elijah to the heights of heaven, he sent his arrow-like rays of light into dark places, and so read the secrets of men. As an all-seeing god he was frequently invoked in oaths. At nightfall he plunged back into Oceanus, for this broad river was supposed to encircle the flat earth, his immersion being accompanied by a hissing noise. Here he rested and bathed, and during the night travelled in a huge cup back to the east in time for his herald and sacred bird, the crowing cock.

Helios had a headstrong son named Phaeton who one day persuaded his father to let him drive the sun chariot with its fiery horses across the sky. Phaeton proved too weak to check the spirited horses; they bolted, and in their mad flight rushed out of the track of the ecliptic. Falling steeply down to earth they would have set it on fire had not Zeus killed Phaeton with a thunderbolt and allowed Helios to take charge. Phaeton fell into the river Eridanus, and the trail of his crazy drive became the Milky Way. His sisters who had yoked the horses to the chariot were metamorphosed into trees which distilled their tears in the form of a gum known to us as amber.

At Rhodes, an island deemed sacred to Helios, a dedicated chariot and four horses were annually flung into the sea to provide fresh transport for the sun-god. Here stood a great bronze statue to Helios-Apollo, once the pride of the city of Rhodes and one of the 'Seven Wonders' of the world. Some 90 feet high, it was made from spoils left by the Macedonian king Demetrius Poliorcetes, who unsuccessfully besieged the city in 304 B.C. It took twelve years to build and stood for about seventy years until it was thrown down from above the knees during an earthquake about 224 B.C. After lying broken for nearly a thousand years it was bought by a Jew and reconverted into weapons of war.

The present names of the planets are Latin or contractions from the Latin, but they all have Greek equivalents. Hermes (Mercury), one of the numerous natural children of Zeus and the swift messenger of the gods, had many of the characteristics of the Egyptian Thoth and the Babylonian Nabu. Among other attributes he was the inventor of letters, mathematics, and chemistry, he presided over games of chance, and concerned himself with the various aspects of commerce and husbandry. The planet Aphrodite (Venus) was called Phosphoros (Lucifer) or 'the bringer of light' when it appeared as a morning star, and Hesperos (Vesper) when it appeared after sunset in the evening sky. Until about the fifth century B.C. the Greeks failed to identify these two appearances with the one planet. The Pythagoreans, however, learnt to regard the two as one, and Plato writes that: 'The Morning and Evening Star which are one and the same, belong to Aphrodite.' As the goddess of love, the Roman Venus derived most of her characteristics from the Greek Aphrodite who derived from the Syrian Astarte, a version of the Babylonian Ishtar.

Ares, the Greek god of war sometimes identified with Hercules, personified the planet Mars, for both Ares and Hercules were valorous deities. Under Roman rule, Zeus became known as Jupiter, the son of Cronos (Saturn). Cronos perpetrated a monstrous crime against his father, the primeval sky-god Uranos, by castrating him with a sickle-sword or reaping-hook. The severed member fell into the sea, and as the waves and spray gathered about it, the beautiful Aphrodite was born. Cronos in turn was deprived of his power by Zeus, and in Greek art and literature is shown as a sorrowful old man carrying a reaping-hook. He also became identified with the passage of time and the 'Father Time' of story-books; from Cronos we get the modern word 'chronometer'. In quite a different connection we find that Roman harvest festivals were called Saturnalia, and as such were parallels to the Greek Cronia when all social distinctions were for a time abolished.

The Latin names of the five planets of antiquity are also enshrined in the present names of the days of the week. Tuesday, for example, is the day of the Norse war-god Tyr or Tiu, and its French equivalent, Mardi, brings us one step nearer the Italian Marte-di, the day of Mars. Wednesday derives from the day of the great Scandinavian god Woden or Odin, and is Mercury's day. Thor, a Scandinavian god of immense strength who alone could lift the world's heaviest hammer, gives his name to our Thursday, which in Italian is Giove-di, from the Latin Jovis dies or Jupiter's day. Friday derives from Freya, the wife of Woden and mother of Thor. In Italian, Friday is Vener-di, from the Latin Veneris dies, or Venus's day. Saturday ties up with Saturn, and Sunday and Monday pertain to the sun and moon respectively.

When the telescope made possible the discovery of additional members to the solar system, further Greek deities achieved immortality in the heavens. First came the discovery of four of the moons of Jupiter by Galileo Galilei in 1610, moons which were first called 'the Medicean stars' and then Io, Europa, Ganymede, and Callisto in conformity with the old usage of using the names of Greek deities. Jupiter is now known to possess eleven satellites, but only these four larger bodies have been given names; Roman numerals identify the rest. In 1655 Christian Huygens discovered Titan, the first member of Saturn's large family of nine satellites, all of which now bear names from Greek mythology. The first addition to the number of known planets came in 1781, when William Herschel discovered a new planet which he called 'Georgium Sidus' in honour of his patron, George III, and which others called 'Herschel' in honour of its discoverer. The German astronomer J. E. Bode, however, thought it better to keep to tradition, and his suggestion of 'Uranus' received universal adoption. Early in the following century, the first four members (Ceres, Pallas, Juno, and Vesta) of the great family of minor planets (planetoids) which circulates between the orbits of Mars and Jupiter were discovered. Later came the discovery of two more major planets— Neptune in 1845, and Pluto in 1930, both bodies being found by searching in parts of the zodiac where calculations based on irregularities in the motion of Uranus had indicated the presence of disturbing bodies. Altogether, the Graeco-Roman deities are now well represented in the heavens, but only for convenience and uniformity and most definitely for no astrological reason.

Among the many individual states of the Hellenes was Ionia, formed by a group of islands and the coastal strip of western Asia Minor, and containing twelve major cities with the mainland capital, Miletus. Here during the seventh and sixth centuries B.C. were laid the foundations of Greek science. Certain Ionians began to interpret nature in a completely new way, and to adopt an attitude free from religious prescriptions, superstitions, and traditional dogmas. Astrology played no part in this development, although oriental influences were undoubtedly present. The representatives of this new school of thought became known as *philosophers*—a philosopher being a 'lover of wisdom'.

Unlike their oriental counterparts in Egypt and Babylonia, the Ionian philosophers lived in a world of animation, of sea and land interwoven, of hills, promontories, and islands variously patterned under a changeful sky. They were free, imaginative, and poetical folk, intensely curious of the impressive panorama about them. They did not doubt that the world, despite its apparent complexity, was composed of only a single substance. They realized that the changes about them were due, not to the caprices of gods, but to the operations of known physical processes. These processes, they believed, operated throughout nature—even to the remote domain of the fixed stars. Appearances in the natural world were therefore regarded as being caused by the regular interplay of the different states of a single substance.

For Thales of Miletus, engineer, politician, and founder of the Ionian school, everything sprang from water. In accordance with Egyptian traditions, this water was a kind of sublimated watery essence—a mobile, infinite, and divine agent. From it was born the flat disk of the earth, with Delphi as the navel; on it the earth floated—a living organism in a seminal fluid.

Thales' travels in Egypt no doubt gave rise to this particular choice of the watery element, and certainly to his knowledge of geometry. As we have already seen, the geometry of the Egyptians was subservient to their practical needs, and never crystallized into a deductive system of thought. Thales had only to pick up a few of the basic properties of the triangle and circle to see what the Egyptians had missed—that general principles underlaid the construction and various relationships between different figures. 'Thales of Miletus,' records Diogenes Laertius, 'having learnt geometry from the Egyptians, was the first to inscribe a right-angled triangle in a circle, whereupon he sacrificed an ox.'

If we accept the doubtful testimony of Herodotus in this connection, Thales sometime before 585 B.C. predicted a solar eclipse. He had no means of knowing if it would appear total from Ionia, nor was he aware of the saronic eclipse cycle, for the Babylonians had yet to discover it. Yet, according to Herodotus, the eclipse took place whilst the Lydians and Persians were engaged in battle, and was so complete that 'day was turned into night'. 'Thales of Miletus', the historian relates, 'had foretold this loss of daylight to the Ionians, fixing it within a year in which the change did indeed occur. So that when the Lydians and Persians saw the day was turned into night they ceased from fighting, and both were the more zealous to make peace.' Various dates for this eclipse have been suggested, but most authorities favour the afternoon eclipse of May 28, 585. If Thales did indeed predict this event, even if only 'to within a year', its occurrence must have quite offset the impression given by another story according to which he is said to have fallen down a well whilst watching the stars.

Anaximenes, another Ionian, made air the primary substance, whilst Heraclitus of Ephesus considered that fire was both the symbol of change in nature and the substratum of all things. To the sceptical Democritus of Abdera, and also Leucippus of Miletus, the universe was composed of an infinite number of indivisible, finite bodies called atoms. They had different sizes, and in infinite space produced an infinite number of worlds.

One of the most interesting and important philosophers of the Ionian school was Pythagoras, a native of the island of Samos and the son of an engraver of talismans. He visited Thales, and at the latter's suggestion spent some years in Egypt to acquire a knowledge of mathematics and something of the mysteries of the East. Upon his return he travelled in Asia Minor and returned to Samos, but his lectures seem to have been coldly received. About 528 B.C. he moved to Croton in southern Italy, where he founded an Orphic mystico-religious brotherhood—a kind of secret society which, unfortunately for historians, credited all its discoveries to its founder. The society made great play with the doctrine of the transmigration of souls, and Pythagoras seems to have been revered as a reincarnation of the Delian Apollo. This doctrine also restricted the Pythagoreans to a vegetarian diet, and they regarded flesh-eating as little better than cannibalism. They believed that numbers are both the patterns and causes of all things—that the universe is the product of harmonious mathematical relationships. Special significance was attached to the regular solids, but most perfect of all was the sphere, just as the circle was the most beautiful of all plane figures. For Pythagoras, therefore, the earth was a sphere, an idea which he does not appear to have extended to the sun and moon. This remarkable decision, so contrary to ordinary experience, had a profound effect on subsequent thought. As we shall see in ensuing pages, only a very small minority of intellectuals thereafter entertained the earlier Greek flat-earth theory.

By the attention they gave to numbers and geometrical figures the Pythagoreans came to develop what can best be called the philosophy of mathematics, a study which led to the discovery of incommensurable numbers like $\sqrt{2}$, $\sqrt{3}$, and $\sqrt{5}$, and to work in the theory of numbers and proportions.

Pythagoras is said to have discovered that the pitch of notes given by a vibrating string varies inversely as the length of the string, also that the lengths which sound a note, its fifth, and its octave are in the ratio 6 : 4 : 3. This idea he applied to the planets, in the belief that their distances are also in musical progression. In their motion through space, therefore, the sun, moon, and planets emit sounds proportional in pitch to their various distances, and, being analogous to the seven strings of Orpheus's lyre, together form celestial music of such sweetness that the gross senses of mankind hear nothing.

The very same idea, even to the consideration of a musical harmony of the spheres, inspired Johannes Kepler 2,000 years later. During the years before 1619, and when Copernican ideas were accepted by only a small minority, Kepler busied himself with all manner of strange analogies between the proportions of the solar system and the relations between the various musical scales. For him the moving earth sounds the notes Mi, Fa, Mi because it is the abode of Mi-sery (Miseria) and Fa-mine (Fames). Mercury and Venus sing high notes, Mars has a tenor part, and slow-moving Jupiter and Saturn supply the bass. Fanciful notions maybe, but both Pythagoras and Kepler believed that harmony was the plan of the structure of the universe. With Kepler it was an ever-present and necessary source of faith and encouragement for one who spent nineteen weary years trying to discover the laws of planetary motion. That he at length succeeded is well known, and with his success faded the last hopes of the exponents of the old Ptolemaic theory.

Pythagoras had a large following in southern Italy, and his school is said to have held large and enthusiastic audiences. An ardent listener and disciple was Theono, the young and attractive daughter of his host, Milo. Despite the disparity of their ages, Pythagoras married her, but their happiness was brief. The authorities at Croton grew suspicious of the mystical practices at the school, and under political pressure from both inside and outside the brotherhood, Pythagoras fled to Tarentum and thence to Metapontum. He died there about 497 B.C. When Cicero visited the city in 78 B.C. he was shown both the house where Pythagoras had died and the tomb in which he was buried.

Although mentally free in their attitude towards nature, the Ionians experienced the trials of foreign domination. First they were conquered by the Lydian tyrant Croesus, whose capital at Sardis became one of the great cultural centres of Asia Minor. In 546 B.C., Harpagus, the general of Cyrus, overran the country, and for nearly fifty years both Ionia and Lydia were vassal states of Persia. Then, with assistance from Athens, the Ionians revolted, but only to be reconquered by the armies of Darius I and to experience strong repressive measures. Miletus fell in 494 B.C. and suffered almost to the point of extermination. 'The Milesians that were taken alive', says Herodotus, 'were sent to Susa; and King Darius did them no harm, but made them dwell by the Red Sea [the Persian Gulf] where the stream of the river Tigris entereth the sea.'

Anaxagoras of Clazomenae in Asia Minor, the last philosopher of the Ionian school, was born about 499 B.C., and therefore grew up under Persian rule. He came from a good Ionian family, and perhaps as a soldier joined the army of Xerxes in 480 as it marched to the Hellespont. The Persian forces crossed by a bridge of boats, by-passed and routed the Spartan army at the pass of Thermopylae, and proceeded to Athens. From a lofty seat on Mount Aegaleos near Athens, Xerxes saw the destruction of his fleet off

Salamis, and alarmed at this reversal of fortune, set out with the bulk of his great army on the long march back to Susa.

Anaxagoras remained in Athens, and by his teaching planted the young growth of Greek science in the mainland. His interests covered a wide field, for he studied anatomy, medicine, mathematics, and astronomy, but in those times these subjects were bracketed under the heading of philosophy. The universe, he thought, was originally a chaos of innumerable 'seeds' in which Mind, or *Nus*, as a corporeal force set up a vortex, and so caused order and form. Astronomy, he believed, was concerned with the study of wholly material bodies. The stars, for instance, are stones made hot by friction and prevented from falling down only by the rapidity of the motion of the vault of heaven. Sometimes the friction engenders sparks, and when these fly out we have the appearances of shooting stars. The moon, he thought, is an inhabited flat disk like the earth, and is diversified by plains and ravines. The sun is a red-hot stone larger than the Peloponnesus, and the great meteoric stone which fell in 468 at Aegos Potami (see p. 70) originally came from it. This idea was slightly in advance of that of Heraclitus the Pythagorean, who thought that the sun is no larger than a human foot!

Anaxagoras was the first philosopher to suggest that the moon shines by reflecting light from the sun, or, as he puts it, that 'the sun puts the brightness in the moon'. This made possible an explanation of eclipses—thus the sun is eclipsed at the time of new moon because the (flat) moon gets in the way and casts its shadow upon the earth. Likewise the moon is eclipsed when the earth's shadow falls on the moon. This shadow, he thought, stretches even to the sphere of the stars, and by shielding them from the sun's bright light, renders them more conspicuous. In this way the girdle of the Milky Way is formed—an ingenious explanation, but patently absurd, since during the course of a year the Milky Way should change its position among the stars. These and other original ideas he passed to his friends and pupils Pericles and Euripides, and through them to Socrates, Plato, and Aristotle.

Pericles, the greatest of all Greek statesmen and the leader of Athens in 'the Golden Age', had many enemies. They made several attempts to ruin his reputation, but failing in these, they attacked him through his friends. His mistress Aspasia, his teacher Anaxagoras, and his friend Pheidias (the famous sculptor and superintendent of the building of the Parthenon), were all accused before the people. Pheidias and Anaxagoras were both charged with impiety. Pheidias was imprisoned for the rest of his life and died from disease. Anaxagoras was condemned to death, but through the eloquence of Pericles, had the sentence transmuted to a fine and banishment. Anaxagoras left the Athenian Archelaus to continue his teaching, and retired to Lampsacos in Troad, where he refounded his school. He died about 428 B.C., asking as a last favour that the children of the city should be given an annual day's holiday in his memory.

The influence of Anaxagoras is seen in an anecdote concerned with Pericles and mentioned by Plutarch. Just as Pericles was about to order his fleet to sail, an eclipse of the sun occurred. The growing darkness threw the sailors into the greatest consternation and the pilot, much astonished, regarded it as an adverse omen. Pericles thereupon took a cloak, and covering the pilot's eyes with it, asked him whether this action presaged disaster. Upon his answering in the negative, Pericles told him that whilst the sun was obscured on both occasions, the obscuring body in the sky was not a cloak but the moon.

The teaching of Anaxagoras is also seen at one place in the writings of his countryman and contemporary, Hecateus of Miletus. Like many later poets, Hecateus tells of the mythical island of Hyperborea, where people lived in innocence and perpetual happiness. From this island, he says, the moon appears so large that 'certain eminences of a terrestrial form are plainly seen in it'.

Hecateus also refers to the 'great year', or cycle of nineteen solar years equivalent to 235 lunations, which Meton of Athens, contemporaneous with Anaxagoras, introduced into the Greek calendar. Once every 'great year', says Hecateus, the sun-god Apollo visits the island of Hyperborea and there plays upon the lyre and dances from the time of the vernal equinox until the rising of the *Pleiades*.

Before the time of Meton, about 432 B.C., the Greeks had adopted a year of twelve months of thirty days each. Every three years out of eight they intercalated a thirteenth month, but the arrangement still failed to bring the first day of the month at or near the time of new moon. This proved disastrous for the fixing of festivals and games, and gave rise to the following complaint by the moon in Aristophanes' play *The Clouds*, performed in 423 B.C.

> Yet you will not mark your days
> As she bids you, but confuse them, jumbling them all sorts of ways,
> And she says the gods in chorus shower reproaches on her head,
> When in bitter disappointment they go supperless to bed,
> Not obtaining festal banquets duly on the festal day.

According to Diodorus, a historian of the first century B.C., the so-called *Metonic cycle* commenced on July 16, 433 B.C. It was acclaimed by the crowds assembled at the Olympic Games, adopted in all the cities and colonies of Greece, and by being set in letters of gold on a marble pillar, received the name of 'golden number'. Even so, its success was comparatively short-lived. At the end of the first cycle the same lunations returned on the same days, but not at the same hour and minute, and after four lunations the error had grown to just over a day. Consequently by 357 B.C. the several phases of the moon would be observed to happen a day sooner than the time computed by the calendar. To remedy this defect, Calippus (p. 65), who lived about a century after Meton, introduced an additional leap day once every four years.

Sundials and water-clocks were doubtless introduced into Greece from Egypt, but both items were comparative rarities at the time of Anaxagoras and Meton. Hence when the latter set up a gnomon against the wall of the Pnyx at Athens, its erection was quite an event in the city. Appointments were made with reference to the time when the shadow of the gnomon or style was so many feet long, a mode of reckoning which suggests that the gnomon was of a standard length. In another type of sundial, called the *hemicycle* and said to have been introduced at Athens by Berosus, the shadow of a vertical gnomon fell on the inner surface of a hemisphere. The end of the shadow traced a curve, the position of which depended on the time of the year. In both cases temporal hours were used, the interval between sunrise and sunset being divided into twelve equal parts regardless of the season. On cloudy days or at night, reference was made to water-clocks, and sometimes in the homes of the wealthy a slave was appointed to announce the passing hours.

Small water-clocks akin to the hour-glass were also used in Greek judicial courts to regulate the time allowed for speeches. 'This', says an ancient chronicler, 'was to prevent babbling; that such as spake ought to be brief in their speeches.'

Xerxes never returned to the Greek mainland, and the armies he left behind in the Peloponnesus and in Ionia were eventually liquidated by the combined forces of the Greeks. Athens was by no means freed from war, however, and until 440 B.C. her armies were engaged in keeping rebellious vassal states in order. Then nine years of peace descended, during which Pericles, as the unrivalled leader in Athens, adorned the city with public buildings of great beauty. In 431 fresh hostilities broke out between Athens and Sparta and gradually spread over the entire Peloponnesus. This ruinous war lasted for twenty-seven years, at the end of which time Athens found itself overwhelmed with calamity. A plague early in the period had carried off Pericles and a quarter of the population; a disastrous campaign in Syracuse saw the loss of the greater part of the navy; subject-states like Chios, Lesbos, and Rhodes were in revolt. In 404 Athens capitulated, her fortifications were demolished, and after a kind of quisling rule, her embittered and disillusioned people faced a future of temporary poverty, unemployment, and distress. Against this troubled

E

background the philosopher Socrates left natural philosophy and sought spiritual values, Plato abandoned thoughts of a political career and travelled abroad, and the cynical Diogenes retired to live in a tub, preferring the company of pigs to that of men.

Socrates, born near Athens about ten years after the battle of Salamis, was the great figurehead of the Athenian school of philosophy. At an early age he joined up with Archelaus, the pupil of Anaxagoras, and with him visited Asia Minor; he also served with distinction in the Peloponnesian War. On settling in Athens, and convinced that he was the chosen agent in a divine plan, he gathered around him a circle of associates and attempted the moral re-education of his fellow-men. Guided by an inner voice, he is said to have wandered Athens ever seeking opportunities for awakening and guiding in boys, youths, and men moral consciousness and the consequences of the Delphic motto: 'Know thyself'. Convinced that the underlying realities of the universe are not material things but spiritual values, he introduced the then novel idea of the soul—an essentially immaterial and divine entity which, as the very essence of our personality, should receive all our care and attention. Hence Socrates extended philosophy to embrace ethical values and moral problems. For him, the problems of human nature were far more interesting than those of the physical world. He considered astronomy important only because its study stimulates and ennobles the mind. Likewise geometry trains the mind in accurate deduction. True knowledge, the knowledge of realities, is obtainable only by the exercise of pure reason. 'With Socrates,' writes Aristotle, 'the enquiry into nature came to an end.'

These ideas, and more especially the ironies, rebukes, and adverse criticism which Socrates levelled at rich and poor alike, gained him many enemies. Finally, and mainly for political reasons, he was accused of corrupting the youth of Athens and despising the deities of the State. Convinced of the immortality of the soul and of his own divine mission, he died with composure

and cheerfulness in 399 B.C. by drinking the prescribed hem-
lock.

Plato was born at Athens in 428 B.C., became a follower of
Socrates at the age of twenty, and was barely twenty-four when
Athens fell to the Spartans. After the death of Socrates he left
Athens and pursued knowledge in Egypt and southern Italy. For
a time he also attended the court of Dionysius I, the tyrant
of Syracuse. His journeys over, he founded an Academy or
School beside the olive groves of Cephisus just outside Athens.
Apart from two voyages to Sicily to direct the education of
Dionysius II, he remained at the Academy until his death in
347.

Plato taught, among other things, that the world of the senses
is illusory and unreal in the sense that realities or 'idealities' are
laid up in heaven and are discernible only with 'the eye of the
soul'. Thus 'the broideries in the heavens' merely illustrate far
more perfect 'broideries' which the eye cannot see, but which can
be studied by reason alone and through geometry. The heavenly
bodies are admitted to be far more perfect than anything on the
earth, but behind them lies perfection itself, and this is denied to
mortal vision. Sharing in this perfection is God, the supreme
good, the highest-grade soul, and the ultimate source of all
motion. Next in the divine hierarchy come the stars, which Plato
regarded as being eternal and divine animals, and the last resting-
places of the souls of the good and just on the earth. The planets,
too, are divine animals, and their orderly behaviour clearly indicates that they possess superhuman intelligences.

'The true astronomer', Plato writes, 'must be the wisest of
men, understanding by the term, not the man who cultivates
astronomy in the manner of Hesiod and all others of that type,
concerning himself only with such things as risings and settings,
but the man who investigates the seven revolutions included in
the eight revolutions, each of the seven describing its own circle
in a manner such as would never be easily comprehended by any
one unless he possessed extraordinary powers.'

On such bases, astronomy presented few problems. Little was to be gained by observing the heavens, for the observable cosmos was an illusion, howbeit a magnificent one. Such problems as existed were no different from those of geometry—you just had to sit down and work them out.

CHAPTER IV

CONCENTRIC SPHERES

Round a fix'd axis roll the starry skies:
Earth, even balanc'd, in the centre lies.

Aratus

BY the fourth century B.C. the Greeks had made no attempt to develop systematic observation in astronomy. Instead, they fostered geometry and a geometrical way of thinking, seeking how best to describe the motions of the heavenly bodies in terms of circular orbits. At first, and as we have just seen in connection with the Ionian school, they considered the earth to be a floating body encompassed by the spherical heavens which contained physical entities like the sun, moon, planets, and comets. Until the time of Pythagoras the earth was also taken to be flat, but the necessity for a supporting medium was questioned by Anaximander, the successor to Thales. In his opinion the earth hung freely in space, for there was no other body in space large enough to cause it to fall in any one particular direction. By the Pythagoreans the earth was regarded as being spherical, unsupported, and centrally placed in the universe. Around it, and in increasing order of distance, revolved the moon, sun, and planets, all in circular orbits, whilst outside the orbit of Saturn (the slowest and hence the most distant planet) the sphere of fixed stars rotated once in twenty-four hours.

Although this was the general descriptive trend, individual philosophers differed on important points. About 400 B.C., Philolaus, a Pythagorean contemporaneous with Socrates, perceived that the apparent motion of the stars could be accounted for by making the spherical earth revolve round a central point once in twenty-four hours. He imagined that a central but invisible and controlling principle of fire existed at this point, which he called 'the Hearth of the universe, the House of Zeus, the Mother of the Gods, the Altar, Bond and Measure of Nature'. To bring the number of bodies encircling this central fire to the mystical number ten, Philolaus postulated the existence of a 'counter-earth' which kept pace with the earth and so remained eternally invisible. Heraclitus or Heraclides, another Pythagorean and a pupil of Plato, suggested that the earth might just as well rotate on an axis once in twenty-four hours, for in so doing it would give rise to the same diurnal appearances. He even took the then bold step of making both Mercury and Venus revolve about the sun, which in turn revolved about the rotating earth once a year.

Differences of opinion arose over the essential nature of the heavenly bodies. The Ionians, and especially Anaxagoras, thought that the cosmos was wholly material, although Thales for one lodged divinity in that materiality. Plato, in contrast, looked on the heavenly bodies as divine animals moved around the earth by chanting Sirens. Like Pythagoras, he believed that the cosmos is ruled by harmony, so that the distances of the planets are analogous to the tones of a musical scale. To find this scale he combined the numbers of two geometrical progressions—1, 2, 4, 8, and 1, 3, 9, 27—to obtain the series 1, 2, 3, 4, 8, 9, 27. Plato used the planetary order apparently first given by Anaxagoras— namely, moon, sun, Mercury, Venus, Mars, Jupiter, and Saturn —so that these bodies are severally distant from the stationary earth by the seven numbers of the combined scale given above. Their motions derive from the exertions of the three Moirae or goddesses of fate. Klotho directs the motion of the entire heavens and rules the present; Atropos moves the planets with their various motions against this general motion, and rules the future; Lachesis assists in both operations. Klotho is also a spinning fate, and Plato regarded the entire cosmos as spinning on the spindle of Necessity.

Yet another approach, and one made by Eudoxus and Calippus, two pupils of Plato at the Academy, was to shelve the problem of the physical or divine nature of the planets and to concentrate on working out a geometrical system which would account for their known wanderings.

Eudoxus was born at Cnidos in Asia Minor about 408 B.C. At the suggestion of Plato, and furnished with letters from the King of Sparta to the King of Egypt, he spent some months at Heliopolis learning mathematics and details of the planetary motions. Upon his return to Cnidos via Athens he set up an observatory, and settled down to mathematical studies and to the elaboration of what became a most ingenious model of the planetary system.

To describe the erratic motions of the planets (as seen from the earth) with their stationary points, advances, and retrogressions, Eudoxus fixed each body to a sphere and arranged for the latter to interlock and to be concentric with three other spheres. At the centre of the entire system was the earth, whilst the outer sphere constituted the sphere of fixed stars which by its rotation gave rise to the diurnal motion of the sky. Each planet-bearing sphere also rotated in the same direction and with the same uniform diurnal speed, but its three associated auxiliary spheres, all attached together and moving with different but uniform speeds about axes suitably inclined, gave rise to the contrary motion of the planet itself. The sun and moon each required three spheres for the portrayal of their apparent motions, so that the entire system required a total of twenty-seven spheres. The system subsequently developed by Calippus along the same lines required as many as thirty-four spheres 'to account for the phenomena'. By these geometrical as distinct from mechanical means the two astronomers were able to represent the then known motions of the planets (except in the difficult case of Mars) quite satisfactorily.

Aristotle, a native of the Greek colony in Chalcidice and the pupil of Plato at the Academy, attempted to combine the oversimplified aesthetic system of Plato with the main features of the geometrical model of Eudoxus. Aristotle considered that the outer starry sphere is under the direct control of the *Primum Mobile* or 'Unmoved Mover', and gives rise to the perpetual motion of an inscribed set of thick concentric shells. These shells are crystalline, and therefore highly transparent, and to each of them in turn are attached the planets, the sun, and the moon, all in the order inwards of their apparent periods of revolution— namely, Saturn, Jupiter, Mars, Venus, Mercury, sun, and moon. Aristotle thus followed Plato in assigning this order to the planets, but he diverged completely from the mathematical spirit of Eudoxus by giving the spheres a physical interpretation. In his system, moreover, each planetary sphere or shell automatically shares in the general diurnal motion. But as the planets have their own individual motions among the stars, he perforce added a set of 'unrolling' shells below each planetary shell. These both moved the planet against the general diurnal motion and neutralized all outside motions except that of the sphere of stars. Altogether, fifty-five shells were required, but the system still failed to account for all the observed phenomena. A set of homocentric spheres, for instance, will not account for the observed variations in the brightnesses of the planets, especially in the cases of Mars and Venus, nor will it yield variations in the apparent sizes of the sun and moon—variations which sometimes occasion an annular as distinct from a total eclipse of the sun.

Since the source of all motion is the eternal *Primum Mobile* of the starry sphere, Aristotle's universe is at once single, finite, purposeful, and eternal. Beyond the sphere of the moon the heavens are considered to be ethereal, unchanging, and incorruptible. The only form of change is not one of substance but one of position, that is, of uniform and perpetual motion in a circle. In the Middle Ages, when Aristotle's system became the accepted cosmology for the Holy Roman Church, the *Primum Mobile* was interpreted as God. For Aristotle it was an immovable, non-material, but sentient agent. It had a soul or *anima* whose perfection the souls of the planetary spheres strive to copy, and in doing so, maintain their circular motions.

For Aristotle the earth is at the centre of the universe because this is its proper and natural place in the scheme of things. It does not rotate because when a stone is thrown upwards it falls back to its point of projection. In any case, uniform circular motion is more appropriately vested in the sublime sphere of stars than in the gross and humble earth.

Aristotle was the first to give definite reasons for the Pythagorean belief that the earth is a sphere, and the figure which he gave for its diameter (12,460 miles) is excessive but not unreasonable. He said that during an eclipse of the moon the edge of the earth's shadow is always circular, so that the body which casts the shadow must be circular also. Important in this respect was his knowledge that a slight journey north or south changes both the appearance of the horizon and the altitudes of stars in the sky. The crescent form of the waxing moon shows that the moon is also spherical, and he argued that all other heavenly bodies must therefore have this shape. 'That the shape of each star is spherical', he writes, 'is the most reasonable view to take. For, since it has been shown that it is not their nature to move of themselves, and Nature does nothing without reason or uselessly, it is clear that she gave to the immovable bodies the shape least adapted for movement. The least adapted is the sphere, because it has no organs to move with; hence the mass of each star must clearly be spherical.'

With Aristotle there originated the doctrine that change and corruption are confined to the regions below the crystalline sphere of the moon—the 'sublunar sphere'. Here everything is composed of combinations of four elements—earth, air, fire, and water, on which operate the principles hot, cold, dry, and moist. Earth and water have 'natural tendencies' to go towards the centre of the world, hence they make up our motionless globe, while air and fire possess the principle of levity and encompass it about, the fire rising above the air. Comets, and 'meteors', like shooting stars, aurorae, and thunderbolts, are therefore confined to the sublunar sphere. They are all formed, Aristotle thought, by dry and hot inflammable exhalations which rise from the earth and become ignited by friction in the upper and fiery layers of the atmosphere. If the exhalation burns rapidly we see a shooting star; if it is less inflammable and extensive, a comet is generated. Even the Milky Way is formed in a similar manner, except that the exhalations are then secreted by the stars and form a permanent accumulation of ignited vapour against the vault of heaven.

Having given comets a meteorological nature, it was natural that Aristotle should regard them as signs of the weather. Since comets have a dry and fiery nature, frequent cometary appearances denote dry and windy years: 'When the stone at Aegos Potami fell out of the air,' he writes, 'it had been carried up by a wind and fell down in the daytime—then too a comet happened to have appeared in the west. And at the time of the great comet [371 B.C.] the winter was dry and north winds prevailed, and the wave [a tidal wave which engulfed the towns of Helice and Bura] was due to an opposition of winds. . . . Again in the archonship of Nichomachus [341–340 B.C.] a comet appeared for a few days about the equinoctial circle (this one had not risen in the west), and simultaneously with it there happened the storm at Corinth.'

Aristotle erred when he regarded comets as random phenomena in the earth's atmosphere. Instead, they circulate about the sun as do the planets, but generally in highly elliptical orbits and with periods which range from a few years to many thousands of years. The ancients recorded only those larger long-period comets which developed impressive tails by reason of their great sizes and comparatively close approaches to the sun and earth. Yet even these giants lost their tails when they drew remote from the sun. To the naked eye they had every appearance of being chance visitors, coming as if from nowhere, and fading away without leaving a trace behind. There were no means then available, moreover, for finding their distances—their comparatively rapid motions and changes in aspect supported the notion that they were atmospheric, and their apparently fixed direction when viewed by observers over a large area at any one time indicated that they were at a great height. They also often appeared well outside the zodiac (for cometary orbits are often highly inclined to the ecliptic), and several moved into northern parts of the sky. These facts, coupled with their sudden, changeful, and apparently random appearances, successfully concealed their true nature from the Greeks, and if we are to believe Epigenes, who studied among them, from the Chaldeans also.

Anaxagoras believed that a comet is a concourse of planets, that is, two or more planets so nearly in the same direction that they appear to form one large object of unusual brightness. Had he possessed planetary tables like those of the Chaldeans he would, of course, have seen the patent absurdity of this theory. Aristotle was more cautious. He noted that many previous comets appeared outside the zodiac—and when several of the planets were also visible. He was also aware that many previous comets were very extensive objects, and that those seen in the time of Anaxagoras disappeared without setting—they just faded away after a few days of brilliance and left no traces of a star behind.

Aristotle observed at least two comets. One was so faint that he could see its tail only by averted vision, that is, by not looking direct but to one side of the object. It was far removed from the ecliptic and in the constellation of the Greater Dog (*Canis Major*). He also saw the comet of 371 B.C., which appeared in a clear winter sky. Although its head set just after the sun, the tail extended to the belt of Orion—over a third part of the sky. On two occasions he had seen Jupiter come into conjunction with a bright star, but the planet grew no tail.

Since the tails of comets are both generated in the vicinity of the sun and are always directed away from it, they point upwards in the morning and evening sky. This appearance, not unlike that of a rising flame, perhaps encouraged the Aristotelian notion that comets are exhalations in the upper atmosphere. To his more credulous compatriots, however, comets often had the appearance of a mass of flowing hair or of a shining, poised sword—interpretations which encouraged omen-seekers to predict dire and bloody calamities. Unfortunately for the cause of science, these false and misleading conclusions became attached to the comets themselves. Instead of being objects requiring study they were regarded as harbingers of misfortune; their colour was sanguine, the tail was a stream of flaming hair, rough, and shaggy, their light was a baleful glare. Hence for Homer the helmet of Achilles shone 'like the red star, that from his flaming hair shakes down diseases, pestilence, and war'.

The physical connection between comets and meteorites is a comparatively recent discovery made possible only after the properties of cometary orbits and meteor showers became well established. In the time of Aristotle, meteorites were popularly regarded as divine missiles hurled down from the home of the gods. As such, those that were found were worshipped, and a temple was often built over the ground made holy by the impact. Thus at Aphaca in Syria a meteorite fell which was considered to be Astarte herself, and a temple to that goddess was promptly reared over the spot. The Palladium or sacred image of Pallas Athena at Troy was in all probability a meteorite, as was the sacred shield of Numa and the image of Diana at Ephesus 'which fell down from Jupiter'. Another meteorite which fell near Homo in Syria was set up in a large temple there and worshipped as an image of the sun-god Elagabalus. Yet the meteorite which fell at Aegos Potami in Thrace in 468 B.C. was apparently left alone for several centuries afterwards. Pliny the elder saw it in the first century A.D. and described it as having a burnt surface and being as large as a chariot.* Anaxagoras believed it came from the sun, but we know now that in all probability it came from Halley's comet, which made a close approach to the earth in 467 B.C.

After the death of Plato in 347 B.C., Aristotle moved to the

---

* The largest known meteorite is one of 60 tons which fell in South Africa. The Ahnighito, the largest meteorite preserved in a museum weighs 34 tons and was found by Eskimos at Cape York in northern Greenland. It was brought to the United States of America by the explorer Robert E. Peary in 1897 and is now in the Museum-Hayden Planetarium, New York City. Meteorites range in size from small pebbles to these giants, and about 1,400 specimens have now been found.

court of his friend Hermeias, Tyrant of Atarneus, a city-state on the north-western coast of Asia Minor. Here he married Pythias, the adopted daughter of Hermeias, but his domestic bliss was of short duration. Trouble with the Persians led to the death of Hermeias, and Aristotle fled to Mytilene on the island of Lesbos. Two years later, in 342, he accepted an invitation to join the court of Philip of Macedon, there to undertake the instruction of the thirteen-year-old Prince Alexander, the future Alexander the Great. Aristotle spent seven comparatively happy years in Macedonia, being treated by his employers with kindness and respect. Alexander came to the throne in 335, whereupon Aristotle was invited to teach at the Lyceum, a gymnasium sacred to Apollo Lyceus and assigned to him by the Athenian state. Here he lectured on many subjects, strolled and discoursed in the shade of the trees with his special scholars, and composed the greater part of his numerous works. In his work he was assisted by his former pupil, Alexander, then campaigning in the Near East, for in addition to large sums of money, Alexander sent him texts, botanical specimens, and zoological curiosities from many parts of Syria, Egypt, and Mesopotamia.

Callisthenes, the son of Aristotle's niece and scientific adviser and historian to the Macedonian army, naturally saw that his great-uncle received only the best and most valuable scientific curiosities. Thus when the army halted at Babylon after defeating the Persian hosts near Arbela, Callisthenes was shown tablets of eclipse records together with a section of the observations which, as we saw in Chapter II, dated back to 747 B.C. These he apparently sent to Athens, together with a report on the state of Babylonian astronomy. At any rate, and speaking of an occultation of Mars by the moon, Aristotle adds: 'Such observations have been made on the other planets for many years by Egyptian and Babylonian astronomers; and many of these have come to our knowledge.' There is certainly no truth in the statement, made by his great commentator, Simplicius, that the oriental records extended back some 31,000 years!

Unfortunately, Callisthenes was a pompous and opiniative man, and his remarks more often than not gave offence to Alexander and his friends. It was not long before the savant over-stepped the bounds of diplomacy. He was accused of being involved in a plot against Alexander's life, cast into prison, and is said to have died of disease seven months later.

With the death of Alexander in 323, public opinion in Athens turned against the Macedonian overlords and their friends. Since it was impossible to associate Aristotle with any political activity, a trumped-up charge of impiety was made, but the philosopher successfully escaped before his trial and fled to Chalcis in Euboea. He died there in 322, at the age of sixty-three.

Unlike Plato, Aristotle appreciated to some extent the importance of the discipline of observation and experiment in scientific enquiry. The value of his vast biological work, for instance, rests largely on his own findings—on the direct observation of the habits and life-cycles of bees, fishes, and mollusca. Yet his fondness for large-scale generalizations, and the obvious limitations of time and place often undid his good intentions. Content with no less than the complete survey of all animate nature, he perforce relied on second-hand and hearsay evidence, and so opened the door to irrationality. In astronomy he made a few observations of his own—of comets, aurorae, and occultations—yet he aspired to frame the entire cosmos. Many modern cosmologists, of course, do the same thing, but they can draw on a tradition and wealth of observational material which was denied to Aristotle. He was, without doubt, well-informed about previous work, and although he compromised, his was a sincere attempt to describe the cosmos in physical terms. He could not know that his system, his physics, and his logic would one day so shackle human thought as almost to extinguish the spirit of science.

It is interesting to find that different peoples with different customs and environments interpret the star patterns differently. To the ancient Egyptians, for example, the *Pleiades* sometimes represented a heap of grain, and sometimes the brush of the tail of an ox. To the ancient Greeks they were a mother and her daughters transformed into stars so as to escape the evil intentions of the amorous huntsman, *Orion*. Yet to a certain tribe of American Indians the stars of *Orion* represented merely a stack of dried manioc. To the Hindus the bright star *Procyon* represented their monkey-god Hanuman, and the seven stars of the Plough or Great Bear represented seven holy men. In ancient China, however, this familiar group represented a bushel or measure of corn, the unnaturally long tail of the Bear being the handle of the measure. To the Sumerians, both the Great and Little Bear were two waggons or wains, yet we have already seen that the Egyptians considered the larger constellation to be the haunch of an ox. In England the Great Bear is still popularly called 'Charles' Wain', this name being a corruption of 'churl's wain' or peasant's cart, while a popular name for it in America is 'The Dipper'.

Homer says that the Great Bear 'is also called by the name of the Wain' and that it 'turns about heaven's axle tree' (the north celestial pole) and 'holds ope a constant eye upon *Orion*'. While the other constellations descend below the horizon and so become immersed in the waters of Oceanus, the Wain 'alone is without lot in Oceanus' bath'. In those times the Pole Star or *Polaris* at the tip of the tail of the Little Bear was much nearer to the north celestial pole than it is today. It offered an excellent indication of the north for mariners at sea, and it is said that Thales, like the Phoenicians, used the Little Bear instead of the Great Bear for finding the north celestial pole.

Many of our constellations are called after equivalents of their Greek names, and several illustrate characters or objects in Greek myths and legends. Six constellations, for example, centre about the story of *Perseus* and *Andromeda*. *Perseus* is shown as coming to the rescue of *Andromeda*, a virgin of wondrous beauty whom he found chained to a rock as an offering to the sea-monster *Cetus*. In his hand he carries the gory head of *Gorgon Medusa*, on whose forehead is the variable star *Algol*, 'the Demon', so named by the Arabians. At the sight of the frightful Gorgon's head with its hair

73

of serpents, the sea-monster is said to have been turned into stone, whereupon *Perseus* released *Andromeda* and duly married her. Nearby in the sky are *Cepheus*, the father of *Andromeda*, and his wife *Cassiopeia* whose seated figure involves the five stars of the conspicuous W in our northern skies. The sixth figure of the group is *Pegasus*, the winged horse which sprang from the body of Medusa and which the hero Bellerophon tamed by using a celestial bridle.

Another group of six constellations appears to illustrate a Deluge narrative, for the figures are all of a watery nature. We have the Ship (*Argo Navis*), the Raven (*Corvus*, a bird of prophecy), and the Dove (*Columba*), the Water Serpent (*Hydra*) upon which *Corvus* has just landed, the Altar (*Altar*), and the Man-headed Horse (*Centaur*).

In another part of the sky there appears the majestic figure of *Orion* with his bright belt and sword, and accompanied by the two hunting dogs *Canis Major* and *Canis Minor*. With them are the Hare (*Lepus*), and the Bull (*Taurus*), whose lowered head suggests that he is about to give battle. A curious legend concerns the birth of *Orion*. Hyrieus of Boeotia dearly wished for a son, and the gods granted his request by urinating on the hide of an ox which they then buried for ten lunar months. At the end of this time the spirited *Orion* sprang from the earth and began his amorous adventures. On one occasion he met Pleione and her virgin daughters, and pursued them with such ardour that Pleione prayed to the gods for safety. Her prayer was answered, but in such a way that both hunter and hunted were metamorphosed into stars. Thus Pleione and her daughters now appear as the *Pleiades*, a fine open cluster of stars which the early Greeks regarded as a separate constellation, but which later astronomers incorporated in the Bull.

The *Pleiades* are further immortalized in the beautiful lines of Aratus, a poet of the third century B.C.

> Near his [Perseus] left knee the Pleiads next are roll'd,
> Like seven pure brilliants set in ring of gold.
> Though each one small, their splendour all combine
> To form one gem, and gloriously they shine.

Their number seven, though some men fondly say,
And Poets feign, that one has pass'd away.
Alcyone—Celoeno—Merope—
Electra—Taygeta—Sterope—
With Maia—honour'd sisterhood—by Jove
To rule the seasons plac'd in heaven above.
Men mark them, rising with the solar ray,
The Harbingers of summer's brighter day—
Men mark them, rising with Sol's setting light,
Forerunners of the winter's gloomy night.
They guide the ploughman to the mellow land—
The sower casts his seed at their command.

The last seven lines of this extract refer to the time before the calendar reform initiated by Julius Caesar in 45 B.C. when the Greeks and Romans were without the advantages of even the simplest form of calendar or almanac. Shepherds, farmers, and husbandmen therefore relied largely on the dispositions of star groups in the evening sky for deriving some idea of the time of year. Homer regarded *Sirius*, 'the star which rises in late summer', as a 'baleful sign, for it brings to mortals much fiery heat'. According to Hesiod in the eighth century B.C., 'Sirius parches head and knees and the skin is dry through heat'—hence men are made feeble during the 'dog-days' but 'women are most wanton'. The first appearance of the 'Atlas-born' *Pleiades* indicated that reaping could commence, whilst their disappearance marked the beginning of ploughing. 'Forty nights and days they are hidden and appear again as the year moves round, when first you sharpen your sickle.' The spring, says Hesiod, begins when *Arcturus* is seen to rise above the eastern horizon in the late evening, whilst its heliacal rising in the morning denotes the beginning of the grape harvest. Autumnal sowing and preparations for the commencement of winter begin with the early setting of *Orion* and the *Hyades*.

This rudimentary star-lore naturally accumulated over the centuries, but it was never written down except when poets borrowed some of the more colourful fragments. At his farm and among his vines, the Roman poet Virgil tested old agricultural customs and

F   75

wrote of the constellations, the tillage of fields, and sowing times for beans, millet, and clover. In addition, items of weather-lore and agricultural magic became infused into this scheme, and with them the suggestion of astrologically propitious days. The late rising of *Arcturus* the 'storm-star' heralded the first equinoctial storms, and both *Capella* and the Bull were regarded as rainy signs. 'Black spots on the sun and moon', writes Aristotle's pupil Theophrastus in a book on winds and weather, 'indicate rain; red spots show wind.' A work by Aratus, the *Diosemeia*, is devoted to this latter aspect, for it consists entirely of weather prognostics in verse for seamen, shepherds, and husbandmen.

The first complete account of the constellation figures appears to have been written by Eudoxus from a celestial globe which had been brought from Egypt and exhibited at Athens. The globe had figures on it, and Eudoxus was content merely to list the various names and star places. News of this globe came to Antigonus Gonatas, a king of Macedonia, who commissioned Aratus to render an account of it. Rather than give a catalogue of names, Aratus adopted a poetical interpretation. In the poem we note that all the forty-five constellations named are those used today; a number of extra constellations were added later, including several around the south celestial pole which were unknown to the Greeks. Many of the figures were undoubtedly derived from Babylonian sources, although the names of the figures and the main stars are Greek. Some of the names do not tally with those of today. Our zodiacal sign *Libra* (the Scales) is regarded as the Claws of the Scorpion; *Boötes* (the Herdsman) is called *Arctophylax*, the Bear Driver; *Virgo* is identified with Astraea, the goddess of Justice.

Many passages in the *Phenomena*, as the Aratus poem is called, are of great beauty, and it is not surprising that the work received the attention of numerous commentators and translators right up to modern times. In Rome the poet was read from Latin versions prepared by Cicero and Germanicus Caesar, the nephew of the Emperor Tiberius.

Aratus was born about 260 B.C. at Soli in Cilicia, the native province of St Paul, and it is interesting to note that St Paul was apparently quoting from Aratus when on Mars' Hill he said: 'For in Him we live, and move, and have our being; as certain also of your own poets have said, for we are also his offspring.'

With astrological meteorology in the ascendant, the science of meteorology had little hearing in the Greek view of nature. One practical example, however, is available—the so-called 'Tower of the Winds' built at Athens about 100 B.C. to the design of the astronomer Andronicus Cyrrhestes and still standing in its essential parts. It is an octagonal structure and bore sundials on all its eight sides, for the holes which once carried the gnomons can still be seen. Inside was a water-clock, and on the top a weathervane in the form of a triton, but without the signs of the cardinal points. Windvanes were then great rarities, and it was not until the ninth century A.D. that one in modern form was fitted to a church tower. Around the top of the 'Tower of the Winds', a frieze in low relief represents the sons of Aeolus, the god of winds and the happy ruler of the Aeolian islands. Aeolus was supposed to confine the winds in a mountain cavern, letting them out whenever he thought fit or was expressly bidden to do so by Zeus, the weather-making magician of Olympus.

CHAPTER V

ASTRONOMY BECOMES A SCIENCE

For it is no part of the business of an astronomer
to know what is by nature suited to a position of
rest, and what sort of bodies are apt to move, but
he introduces hypotheses under which some bodies
remain fixed, while others move, and then con-
siders to which hypothese the phenomena actually
observed in the heaven will correspond.

Geminus of Rhodes

AFTER his Indian campaign, Alexander returned to Babylon, but died there in 323 B.C. He was buried at Alexandria, the city which he had founded only nine years earlier. By 323 the building work at the new city was well under way, but the initial project was not completed until the middle of the third century B.C. Eventually the city became the hub and focus of intellectual and literary activity in the Mediterranean basin. Seaward stood the massive Pharos lighthouse to guide mariners to the safety of the great harbour. One of the 'Seven Wonders', the lighthouse was reputed to be 400 feet high. To the south lay Lake Mareotis, an important waterway which linked the city with Memphis on the Nile and thence by canal with the Red Sea. Within the city, and each in their own quarters and with a measure of self-government, re-sided Jews, Egyptians, and Macedonians (i.e. Greeks), together with writers, usurers, craftsmen, and fortune-hunters from distant parts of the vast Macedonian empire.

The Greek quarter contained the royal palace, where Ptolemy Soter, one of Alexander's generals, founded a new dynasty which lasted for just over 350 years. Nearby was the gigantic domed temple of the god Serapis, the dead Apis bull which became Osiris, with its great basalt image and large library. The Serapeum thus formed a religious link between East and West, and we are not surprised to find that the worship of Serapis, Isis, and Horus with their elaborate ceremonials proved popular in Rome until the close of the fourth century A.D. But more important from our viewpoint was the library and museum in the Greek quarter. Together they formed an Academy or University, housed an unrivalled collection of several hundred thousand papyri rolls, and contained an observatory and theatre for assemblies and lectures.

Alexandria flourished under the rule of the first three Ptolemies. They were tolerant towards Egypt, allowed the old cults to continue, and even rebuilt and endowed great temples at Dendereh, Memphis, Edfu, and Philae. They regarded themselves as patrons of literature and science, and they became popularly known by such titles as 'the Saviour', 'the Illustrious', and 'the Beneficent'. Thus Ptolemy I, or Ptolemy Soter, organized the collection of thousands of rolls for the Museum library. Like his friend Alexander the Great, he studied as a youth under Aristotle, and for the times was a man of considerable enlightenment. He invited men of letters and learning to work and lecture in the Museum, and he saw that they received first-class hospitality and ample facilities for research. Like Assurbanipal of olden times, he ordered the collection of manuscripts and rolls from all parts of the empire. During his reign the geometer Euclid collected material for thirteen books of his great symposium of geometrical knowledge, the *Elements*, and Archimedes, the Newton of the ancient world, founded the science of mechanics. Archimedes is said to have invented the Archimedean screw during his residence in Alexandria, a device for raising water from the holds of ships and still used in Egypt for raising water.

Ptolemy II, or Ptolemy Philadelphus, commissioned Manetho, an Egyptian priest of the temple at Heliopolis, who knew Greek, to write a history of Egypt, a few fragments of which are still extant. He also ordered the translation of the *Septuagint*, or sacred Jewish books, from Hebrew into Greek. Under his rule the Museum

79

library is said to have acquired the texts and notes which Aristotle bequeathed to his pupil Theophrastus when he fled from Athens. In the dissection rooms of the Museum the anatomist Erasistratus continued and extended the work done by his predecessor, Herophilus. In astronomy, Aristarchus of Samos, an older contemporary of Archimedes, wrote on the sizes and distances of the sun and moon. His was the first scientific attempt in this direction, but since his methods required noting when the moon appeared exactly at the half, and measuring the size of the patch formed by the earth's shadow during a lunar eclipse, it was incapable of yielding accurate results. He made the diameter of the sun, for instance, to be only some six or seven times that of the earth, and estimated that it was distant by about 14,000 earth diameters. He was the first to note that the angular diameters of the sun and moon are about $\frac{1}{2}°$, but seems to have been unaware that the changing distances of these bodies cause fluctuations in their apparent diameters.

By Aristarchus' reckoning, the volume of the sun is some 300 times that of the earth, and this result probably encouraged him in the view that the smaller body perhaps revolves about the larger, rather than vice versa. He was, in fact, the first astronomer to anticipate Copernicus by suggesting that the sun and sphere of fixed stars are at rest and that the planets, including the earth, revolve about the sun. The reason why Mercury and Venus never appear to depart far from the sun is at once explained by placing their orbits within that of the earth, whilst by making the earth rotate on its axis once in twenty-four hours, the sun, moon, and planets all share in the apparent diurnal motion of the vault of heaven. The Babylonian astronomer Seleucus of Seleucia a century later also shared this belief, but he and Aristarchus appear to have been its only supporters. Other astronomers doubtless considered the sun-centred or heliocentric circular orbits too simple an expedient for accounting for the apparently complex planetary motions. For the same reason, and in view of the great changes in the brightnesses of the planets, especially for Venus and Mars, the geocentric circular orbits of Plato and Aristotle were considered to be untenable. A change of viewpoint was evidently necessary, but it was not to be in favour of heliocentric ideas.

Eratosthenes, another Greek scholar and astronomer, worked under Ptolemy III, or Ptolemy Eurgetes. He arrived at Alexandria from Athens in 244 B.C. and became chief librarian at the Museum Library. He was the first to measure the diameter of the earth by a sound astronomical method. This consisted of measuring the midday lengths of the shadows cast by vertical gnomons at Alexandria and Syene, two places almost on the same meridian. The calculated difference in the sun's altitude came to a little more than 7°, and since this is approximately one fiftieth of 360°, Eratosthenes had only to multiply the distance between Alexandria and Syene by fifty to obtain the circumference of the earth. Professional 'steppers' or 'pacers' found this former distance to be 500 stadia, which made the earth's circumference 250,000 stadia —a result which Eratosthenes later corrected to 252,000 stadia. If we adopt the Egyptian value of the stadium, this makes a degree of the meridian equivalent to 68·5 miles and places the earth's diameter at 7,850 miles—only 50 miles short of the true polar diameter! By modern standards, of course, the observations were roughly made, and had Eratosthenes repeated them he would doubtless have arrived at a less striking result. Nevertheless, the figure arrived at did much to encourage the growing belief that the earth is very large—that, as Plato taught, 'we who live in the region from the river Phasis to the Pillars of Hercules [the Straits of Gibraltar] inhabit a small part of it; like to ants or frogs round a pool, so we dwell round the sea; while there are many other men dwelling elsewhere in many regions of the same kind'. A large earth also indicated a large and finite universe, and Archimedes, by sheer calculation, estimated that the latter could contain no more than 10^{63} (or one followed by sixty-three naughts) grains of sand!

Eratosthenes also made an accurate measurement of the tilt of the earth's axis, or, as we say in astronomy, the obliquity of the ecliptic. His value, 22/83 of a right angle, was only seven minutes of arc greater than the actual value at the time. Although he is known primarily for his astronomical work, Eratosthenes was a scholar of immense erudition. Besides writing on many subjects and supervising work in the great library, he also acted as tutor to the son of his royal patron. In his old age he lost his eyesight, and, growing weary of life, is said to have committed suicide by voluntary starvation.

Eratosthenes was also a pioneer in cartography, for he drew the first map which contained the germ of the latitude and longitude framework. Earlier maps, such as those ascribed to Anaximander and Herodotus, extended little beyond the Mediterranean region, and were built largely on guesswork. Eratosthenes availed himself of a few latitude values obtained from observations of the lengths of the midday shadows cast by vertical gnomons at or near the time of the equinoxes. Once the length of the shadow cast by a gnomon of given length is known, the observer can soon calculate the sun's meridian altitude, which at the time of the equinoxes is equal to the latitude of the place of observation. As a result of observations of this nature, Eratosthenes had available the approximate latitudes of Alexandria, Syene, Carthage, Rhodes, and Byzantium. When he had fixed the direction of the latitude line through Rhodes—and he made it pass like a Mediterranean axis between the Pillars of Hercules—he could draw the other latitude lines parallel to it. The determination of meridians, or north-to-south lines, was a more difficult matter, however, for without the magnetic compass it was extremely difficult to obtain bearings. Approximate star observations no doubt enabled him to fix his primary meridian through Rhodes, and to carry it through Syene in the south and near Byzantium in the north. Without the use of chronometers, of course, reasonable accuracy in determining meridians of longitude was non-existent; Eratosthenes no doubt relied on travel records and the directions and distances given by seamen.

Rich sources of geographical information were provided by the records of Alexander's expedition into Bactria and the Punjab which led him almost to the Ganges. Knowledge of the West was partially covered by Pytheas's account of his voyage to the north-east of the Pillars of Hercules. Setting out from Massalia (the site of Marseilles) late in the fourth century B.C., Pytheas had fol-lowed the west coast of Spain and France until he came to Britain. He visited Cornwall, described the mining communities whose tin had for long formed a valuable commodity for the Phoenician and Carthaginian traders, and sailed northwards along the east coast of Britain up to nearly 61° north. At this latitude, and six days' sailing distance from the northern tip of Scotland, he found 'Thule', 'where the sun goes to rest'. 'For it was found that in these regions', he records, 'the night was quite short, consisting in some places of two hours, in others of three, so that only a short interval elapsed from the setting of the sun before it rose again immediately.' Pytheas, of course, was sufficiently well-versed in astronomy to know that if the days of summer at Thule were long, those of winter would be correspondingly short. But we shall never know whether he had reached Iceland, Norway, the Orkneys, or just the Shetland Islands, for unfortunately his accounts of his experiences have been lost, and we have perforce to rely on quotations made by other authors.

Also at Alexandria with Eratosthenes was Apollonius of Perga, who began an immense work on conic sections which more or less exhausted the subject from a purely geometrical viewpoint. He also considered the use of combinations of uniform circular motions—of deferents and epicycles—for representing the move-ments of the planets, an innovation which Hipparchus and Pto-lemy adopted later with surprising success. He it was who ap-parently re-arranged the planets in the order moon, Mercury, Venus, sun, Mars, Jupiter, and Saturn—an order which both Hip-parchus and Ptolemy adopted and which therefore persisted up to the time of Copernicus. From his fondness for observing the moon, Apollonius was nicknamed 'Epsilon', since this letter of the Greek alphabet was by its shape associated with the moon.

Through an action of Berenice, the wife of Ptolemy Eurgetes, we owe the introduction of the constellation Coma Berenices. After her husband's safe return from a punitive campaign she cut off her hair and laid it in the temple of Mars as a votive offering. Next day the hair was missing, and to placate offended royalty more than the affronted deity, the mathematician Cronon adroitly suggested that a new constellation be formed with the name Coma Berenices, or the Hair of Berenice. Berenice, incidentally, went to heaven by a no less direct route, for she was murdered by her son Ptolemy Philopater on his accession to the throne in 221 B.C.

As the Ptolemies intermarried and became more Egyptianized, so their grip on domestic and foreign affairs weakened. A decided moral decline set in after the reign of Ptolemy VI in the second century B.C. Known as 'Physcon' or 'Big Belly', Ptolemy VI was notorious for his cruelty, debauchery, and infamous behaviour. Family feuds led to large-scale murders, and these in turn led to civil strife and national unrest. Leading Alexandrians were persecuted, and many fled from the city to escape otherwise certain death. Perhaps Hipparchus, the greatest astronomer of the pre-Christian era, was among them, for although he resided for a time at Alexandria, he did most of his work in the comparative safety of Rhodes, the sacred island of Helios.

Hipparchus was born in 190 B.C. at Nicaea in Bithynia, Asia Minor, and was therefore a countryman and contemporary of Asclepiades, one of the greatest physicians of pre-Christian times. Of all his works only one text has survived the centuries, and this is a comparatively small one. It is a commentary on Aratus, concerns the seasonal positions, risings, settings, and culminations of the brighter stars, and points out several errors made by Eudoxus and repeated by Aratus. Fortunately, Hipparchus's great successor Ptolemy, writing three centuries later, based his own astronomical work on that of Hipparchus, but because of this it is somewhat difficult to disentangle their individual contributions.

Hipparchus owed much of his success to the fact that he was, as

Ptolemy puts it, 'a lover of toil and truth'. For the first time in Greek astronomy he introduced circular sighting instruments graduated into degrees. These were superior to those used by the late Babylonian school, and they enabled him to determine large relative angular separations with reasonable accuracy. He thus applied, as it were, a more rigorous 'yardstick' to the positions of the sun, moon, and planets relative to the background of stars. With his instruments and water-clocks he made a special study of the planetary motions, and checked his findings with those from early Babylonian and Greek sources preserved in the library of the Museum. As a result he determined the inclinations and orientations of the orbits of the sun and moon, constructed tables of their motions, investigated inequalities in these motions, and predicted eclipses for long periods ahead.

Hipparchus's investigation of the sun's motion is a good example of the rigour and ingenuity which became the hall-mark of all his astronomical work. In the first instance he measured the obliquity of the ecliptic and arrived at the same result as that obtained by Eratosthenes. By comparing his own observations of the sun with others taken by Aristarchus over a hundred years earlier, he then found that the length of the solar or tropical year was short of $365\frac{1}{4}$ days by 4 minutes 48 seconds. Furthermore, the observations revealed that this period is not equally divided between the four astronomical seasons. In travelling through 90° of the ecliptic from the vernal equinox to the summer solstice, for example, the sun takes $94\frac{1}{2}$ days, yet in travelling from this solstice to the autumn equinox it requires two days longer. It therefore spends 187 days in the 180° above the celestial equator, and $178\frac{1}{4}$ days in the 180° below the celestial equator. In addition, there is the fact (known to Hipparchus) that the apparent diameter of the sun is greatest near the winter solstice and smallest near the summer solstice, a variation which clearly indicates that its distance from the earth is not constant.

Hipparchus then had to ask himself why the sun traverses equal arcs in unequal times despite its uniform orbital speed—for, as Geminus of Rhodes writes: 'The hypothesis underlying the whole of astronomy is that the sun, the moon, and the five planets move at uniform speeds in circles, and in a sense contrary to that of the motion of the universe.' Hipparchus had no intention of violating this cherished Greek idea. Instead, he displaced the earth from the centre of the sun's circular orbit, and at once accounted for the inequality of the seasons and the change in the sun's apparent diameter. The sun's orbit thus became an *eccentric* circle, and the distance between the earth and the geometrical centre was determined and called the *eccentricity* of the sun's orbit. Geminus neatly summarizes the new conception. 'The sun, then, moves at uniform speed throughout, but, because of the eccentricity of the sun's circle, it traverses the quadrants of the zodiac in unequal times.'

We see in this example something of what Plato was getting at when he distinguished between the world of the senses and the world of the intellect. In the world of the senses the sun moves with variable speed over different parts of the ecliptic. In the world of the intellect, the 'true' world, an idealized sun moves in a circular orbit with uniform velocity. Unfortunately for the Hipparchic notion, however, it is not the sun which moves about the earth, but the earth about the sun, and with variable velocity in an elliptical orbit, howbeit of small eccentricity. Neither body is divine or eternal, so they lose nothing in prestige by behaving in this non-Hellenic way.

Hipparchus found that the solar motion could also be represented by the epicycle of Apollonius, but he chose the eccentric circle as being simpler. In the former case the sun was made to move in a subsidiary circle or epicycle, the centre of which moved round a larger and earth-centred circle called the deferent. This idea he applied to the motions of the moon and planets, although from lack of observational data for the latter he did not work out a complete epicycle theory.

In 136 B.C. a bright condensed comet appeared in the constellation of the Scorpion and revealed to Hipparchus that the heavens were not as well charted as they could be. To assist in plotting the course of future visitants, and at the same time to detect them more readily, Hipparchus began to note the number, relative brightnesses, and positions of all the brighter stars. As a result he drew up in 129 B.C. a catalogue of 1,080 stars, grouped in forty-eight constellations or 'asterisms', and positioned with reference to the great circle of the ecliptic, that is, in terms of celestial latitude and longitude. This was a new and invaluable departure from the old practice of referring stars to the constellation figures only. Hipparchus furthermore plotted the stars on a large globe (which was at Alexandria in Ptolemy's time), enlarged on Euclid's geometry of the sphere and the various circles which could be inscribed upon it, and in twelve books, now lost, established the foundations of spherical trigonometry.

Although Ptolemy was the last person to mention the existence of the celestial globe of Hipparchus, we are reminded of another globe of great historical interest which was made probably about the same time and certainly before the Christian era. Known as the Farnese Globe, it is supported on the inclined head and neck of a kneeling figure of Atlas. The constellation figures are sculptured in relief on marble, but several are absent, including the Great Bear, the Little Bear, and of course the then undiscovered groups around the south celestial pole. One cannot resist the thought that the globe of Hipparchus was of a more scientific nature than this —that it showed the latitude–longitude framework and was used for plotting star positions.

When he compared his star positions with those made by earlier observers, notably those of the two Alexandrians Aristillus and Timocharis of the time of Ptolemy Soter, Hipparchus found that the bright star Spica of the Virgin had apparently moved nearer to the autumnal equinox by about two degrees in 150 years. This motion, he found, was shared by all the stars: they all possessed a slow west-to-east motion relative to the equinoxes. This effect—the precession of the equinoxes—was a discovery of the utmost importance. The fact that Hipparchus may have been assisted by the writings of the Babylonian Kidinnu, who according to some authorities was the first astronomer to detect precession, does not lessen the value of his own contribution. He showed, in brief, that all the stars are increasing in celestial longitude (reckoned from the vernal equinoctial point which is symbolized by the pair of horns of the Egyptian hieroglyph ♈) by about 45 to 46 seconds of arc annually (actually 50·26 seconds). One result of this we have already seen—that over the course of many thousands of years different stars occupy the vicinity of the north celestial pole. Another effect, linked directly with the above, is that the vernal equinoctial point, situated in the Ram (*Aries*) in the time of Hipparchus, was in the Bull (*Taurus*) about 4000 B.C., and is now in the Fishes (*Pisces*).

Hipparchus probably died between 130 and 120 B.C., leaving behind him a mass of invaluable observational material but no disciple or pupil to carry on his great tradition. Except for a few observations by Posidonius, Geminus, and others, the new science of astronomy was temporarily shelved for another three centuries. Posidonius followed Aristotelian doctrines and made but few observations; he did, however, observe a comet hitherto concealed by the glare of the sun but which became visible during a solar eclipse. He also made a new measurement of the size of the earth, which, although wider from the truth than that of Eratosthenes, was accepted by Ptolemy and his successors without question. The method was a good one, for it was based on the determination of the altitudes of a star seen from two different places on the same meridian. It was spoilt in its execution, however, for Posidonius, observing from Rhodes, selected the bright star Canopus, which just appeared above the horizon. This gave a convenient zero altitude for Canopus as seen from Rhodes, but near-horizon observations of this nature are never reliable, and in any case the star then had a meridian altitude of just over one degree. Posidonius therefore obtained the erroneous value of 180,000 stadia for the circumference of the earth, yielding a polar diameter of only 5,600 miles.

Geminus lived at Rhodes about 70 B.C., and is known mainly for his systematic treatise on astronomy, which dealt with the main features and consequences of the theories of Hipparchus. He discussed the sequence of day and night, the months, years, and seasons, and distinguished between the word 'sign' as used for the twelfth part of the zodiacal circle and the names of constellations called 'signs', for the latter 'sometimes overlap and encroach on preceding and following signs'.

By 120 B.C. Alexandria had already lost the greater part of its supremacy in Greek learning, a decline hastened by the family feuds and moral failings of the later Ptolemies. Rome, moreover, was extending her boundaries, and by 216 B.C. had embarked upon a long period of conflict with Macedonia, then the ruling power on the Greek mainland. Alexandria and Egypt were left alone so long as they offered no interference to Roman plans.

In the first century B.C., Julius Caesar, infatuated with the beauty of Cleopatra, the last reigning Ptolemy, became her consort and hence master of Egypt. But during strife at Alexandria, Caesar set fire to the Greek fleet in the harbour, and the flames are said to have accidentally reached the library of the Museum. Since most of the rolls were destroyed, the Serapeum thereafter became the principal library. A climax was reached in 30 B.C., when Cleopatra, thrice widowed, found Octavian impervious to her considerable charms. Faced with either transportation to Rome as a captive or death at her own hands, she chose the latter by taking the poison of an asp. Octavian, afterwards styled Caesar Augustus, thereupon seized the reins of power, and Alexandria and all Egypt came under Roman administration.

CHAPTER VI

THE DECLINE OF THE GODS

*In the heavens there is nothing fortuitous, un-
advised, inconstant, or variable; all there is order,
truth, reason, and constancy.*

Cicero

LONG before they adopted the deities of ancient Greece the
Romans paid deference to *numena*—elemental spirits, sprites, and
genii—who were supposed to operate in and around their homes
and fields. There were spirits of the hearth, wine-press, beehive,
crossroads, and woodlands, and above all (in place if not in importance) was Jupiter, the spirit of the sky. As the original agricultural settlements fused into the city-state, many of these spirits
acquired new forms and attributes. Both Janus and Jana, for example, were spirits of the door who became sun-god and moon-
goddess respectively. As the guardian deity of gates, and because
every door looks two ways, Janus was represented with two faces.
Even his temple at Rome was little more than an elaborate gateway which faced east and west. Open during times of war and
closed during times of peace, it was closed only four times before
the Christian era.

It is from Janus that we get the name of the month January,
for Janus was not only the porter of heaven but also the god who
opened the year and the seasons. Mars, at first mainly an agricultural spirit, became the god of war; Jupiter became the god of justice, law, and virtue, and with Juno and Minerva formed a divine
trinity, a symbol of the religious majesty of the State.

The third and second centuries B.C. saw the wholesale assimilation of the archaic gods of Rome with the lively company of Olympus. Mighty Zeus was absorbed with Jupiter, the father of the gods and ruler of heaven with his wife Juno, the Greek Hera. Ares became identified with Mars, Athena with Minerva, Poseidon with Neptunus, and Cronus with Saturnus (a mythical king of Italy). By this process the old Roman religion became no religion at all, but the plaything of poets and artists. It was all outside show and glitter, bright enough as a background for plays, festivals, and pageants, but useless as a source of moral inspiration. Small wonder, therefore, that the masses kept faith with the numina of their forefathers or turned to imported oriental cults with their impressive ceremonials, whilst the educated classes embraced the self sufficient and strongly materialistic tenets of the Stoic and Epicurean philosophies.

From time to time, and as their empire expanded and often became unsteady in its distant parts, the Romans sought religious ideas that might unify it into a single society sharing a common loyalty. Until the weaknesses of the Julio-Claudian emperors cheapened it, the idea of emperor-worship instituted at the time of Augustus temporarily achieved this end. There was nothing new in this cult of emperor- or Caesar-worship; we have already seen that the pharaohs were regarded as divinities, or at least as incarnations of the god Ammon or Ra. Alexander the Great, led from one incredible military success to another, also regarded himself as a divinity, and was worshipped as such both before and after his death by the Egyptians.

In the third century A.D., when the northern frontiers of the Roman empire were being pushed in by the Goths, the Emperor Aurelian introduced the Syrio-Celtic cult of sun-worship. He became regarded as the earthly vicar and emanation of 'Sol Invictus', or the 'Unconquered Sun', and so set the stage for the advent of a church-inspired society. The son of a priestess of the sun at Belgrade, he built a magnificent temple to Sol Invictus in Rome and even had coins struck in Sol's honour. Diocletian, notorious for his persecution of the Christians, continued to encourage sun-worship, as did his successor Maxentius, recognized 'Augustus' in 306. Six years later the legions of Maxentius under the banner of Sol Invictus confronted the forces of Constantine under the banner of the Cross, emblem of the Unconquerable Christ. The complete defeat of Maxentius at the battle of Milvian Bridge near Rome, and his death by drowning in the Tiber whilst trying to escape, was regarded by many as a signal triumph of Christianity over paganism in general and sun-worship in particular.

The last Roman emperor to uphold sun-worship was Julian surnamed the Apostate and the nephew of Constantine. He was born at Constantinople in 331, and received a good grounding in the principles of Christianity, but subsequent residence at Athens brought him into direct contact with Greek philosophy and paganism. It was not long before he was an ardent astrologer: 'I was considered a stargazer', he writes, 'even before my beard began to sprout.' He practised divination with unquestioning enthusiasm, regarded the stars as so many visible gods, and made the sun the greatest god of all. In 361, after a successful campaign in Gaul, he was proclaimed emperor in succession to his father, Constantius. This enabled him publicly to avow his paganism, but his championship of Sol Invictus and other pagan cults was suddenly cut short two years later by his death on a Persian battlefield.

A cult closely associated with sun-worship, and one popular with the Roman army, was Mithraism. Mithras, a god with strong solar associations, derived from Zoroastrianism, the official religion of the Persians under the Sassanids. In the pure Zoroastrian faith Mithras was a god of light, the eye of Ahura-Mazda, god of heaven and victor over Angra-Mainyu the power of darkness. In Mithraism, Mithras received strong Hellenistic elements and became the very sun, the heavenly and unconquerable light that protects mankind against evil. Through his sacrifice of a primeval bull the young and virile Mithras gave the promise of eternal life to mankind; through his mediation even the poorest of mortals could rise to the supreme heaven and share in a life of everlasting bliss with the godhead. The background was frankly pagan, yet the compound was so well blended with attractive ingredients, even to the point of suggesting spiritual redemption through voluntary castigations and self-discipline, that it proved a serious rival to Christianity.

Both doctrines had points in common. Mithras, like Tammuz and Adonis (the beloved of Venus), spent half the year in the lower and half in the upper world. Likewise the sun spends half the year below the celestial equator and half the year above it. Likewise Christ was born, gave His moral light to the world, died, and rose again—but without any connection with a seasonal drama. Both Christianity and Mithraism shared a belief in immortality and the importance of moral purity through suffering. Both devolved on the idea (although at vastly different ethical levels) of sacrifice and divine mediation.

That Mithraism had astronomical connections is suggested by inscriptions and paintings which portray a bull (representing the dying year of nature) being attacked by other animals. Mithras, wearing a peaked Phrygian cap and attire, kneels on the bull, grasps its nostrils with one hand, and slits its throat with the other. As the life-blood flows from the unfortunate animal an outstretched serpent attacks the fore-hoof, a devouring dog (*Sirius*) leaps up to the gory neck, and a scorpion nips his genitals—doubtless with more effect than the crab who once pinched the heel of Hercules. Ears of corn (the *Pleiades*) spring from the brush of the bull's tail Egyptian fashion, and hold out the promise of new life. On either side stand Hesperos and Phosphoros, two divine torchbearers, one with his torch inclined upwards, the other with his torch inclined downwards, whilst the entire scene is often framed by the twelve signs of the zodiac. The panel probably perpetuates the time when the vernal equinoctial point fell in the sign of the Bull which therefore ushered in the solar year, and when the autumnal equinoctial point fell in the Scorpion. The two figures seem to represent both the evening and morning aspects of Venus, and their torches, the ascent and descent of the sun from the celestial equator.

Since the sun reaches its lowest noon-day altitude in the northern sky on the 25th December, the time of the winter solstice, this date was chosen for celebrating the nativity of Mithras. On this day his initiates held festivals and kindled lights, the gleaming tapers of which represented the fire of the newborn sun. On this day also the Syrians decorated the pine trees sacred to Adonis, and branches of holly and yellow mistletoe adorned respectively the revels of Saturnus and Diana-Artemis. Thereafter the sun rose with increasing height in the heavens and heralded the approach of yet another spring and the promise of summer fruits. In view of the widespread popularity of this winter festival, the early Western Church chose December 25 for celebrating the nativity of Christ. For similar reasons the festival of His resurrection was celebrated at the time of the full moon on or next following the vernal equinox.

After the battle of Pydna in 168 B.C. the Romans began to have access to the accumulated results of Greek work in astronomy and philosophy; yet in the ensuing centuries they acquired little of the Greek spirit of inquiry. They remained an intensely practical and 'down-to-earth' people; their concern was not with the theory of mathematics but with its applications to architecture, road-building, plumbing, and sewage-disposal. 'The Greek mathematicians lead the field in pure geometry,' Cicero writes, 'while we limit ourselves to the practice of reckoning and measuring.' Hence the Romans exploited terrestrial mechanics and left the celestial aspects severely alone. On the basis that the heavens appeared to be immortal and self-sufficient, whilst their empire needed constant attention, they did their best work in military science and legislation. Their technical achievements led to quick material returns, but the neglect of pure science led at once to an uncritical view of nature and to no theoretical basis for the development of physical conceptions.

The attention which they gave to calendar reform is characteristic of the Roman approach to astronomy. At first their calendar appears to have been a lunar one with twelve months and 354 days to the year, although some Roman authors mention only ten months and 304 days. It is clear, however, that the months were lunar months and that Martius, the month of Mars and our March, was the first month. Aprilis, Maius, and Junius followed, then came six months in the numeiical order Quintilis, Sextilis, September, October, November, and December, and finally Januarius and Februarius. To correlate this year with the seasons and tropical year of 365¼ days, an intercalary month called Mercedonius and consisting of twenty-two or twenty-three days was introduced once every two years.

By the middle of the first century B.C. the Roman calendar was in such a confused state that Julius Caesar requested the Alexandrian mathematician Sosigenes to suggest possible reforms. Caesar was himself an able scholar and mathematician, and through his active interest a completely new calendar was instituted. This took the tropical year of roughly 365¼ days as its basis and dispensed with any attempt to make the years or months conform to lunations. Instead, the phases of the moon were allowed to wander at will through the calendar year. The odd quarter of a day was allowed for by inserting an extra day in the month of February once every four years. This was done by the not too satisfactory expedient of counting February 24 twice, and since this day was the sixth day before the kalends of March, our present 'leap' years were originally called 'bissextile' years. In 45 B.C. the new scheme—the Julian calendar and the basis of our calendar today—came into full operation. Needless to say the previous year, 46 B.C., was one of considerable confusion; it had to be extended to 445 days in order that important festivals connected with the seasons might continue to fall around the right time of the year. The year of 45 B.C. thus began on January 1 insteady of March 1, and in 44 B.C. the month Quintilis was changed to Julius (our July) in honour of Caesar. In 8 B.C. his successor Augustus gave his name to the old sixth-month Sextilis, and was thought to have made it equal in length to July by borrowing a day from February. But the old Roman February (Terminalia) originally had twenty-eight days, and archaeological evidence shows that Sextilis already had thirty-one days before it was renamed August.

The months of the Julian calendar, it should be noted, were originally divided into Nones, Ides, and Kalends in accordance with early Roman custom. The seven-day week, a legacy of the Syrio-Babylonian lunar calendars, again rose into prominence during Christian times. The idea of a holy day or sabbath appealed to Jews and Christians alike, a feature not lost on Constantine the Great when he planned to make Christianity the established religion. Through an edict of A.D. 321, Constantine introduced the seven-day week into the Julian calendar, but without making any allowances for the fact that fifty-two weeks of seven days each do not constitute a 365-day year. Hence consecutive New Years failed to begin on Sunday, the first day of the Christian week, and various Church festivals, including Christmas Day, wandered freely among the week-days.

Practically minded Romans also exercised their ingenuity by designing and constructing elaborate sundials and water-clocks. Constructional details were given by Vitruvius Pollio, an architect and military engineer under Caesar, who seems to have borrowed some of his ideas from Ctesibius of Alexandria. Not only did the designs for water-clocks ensure that the water-pressure above the orifice remained constant, but all kinds of devices were used to translate rise or fall of water-level into a form of circular motion. In one case a vertical rack was attached to the float, and as it moved upwards it drove a set of cog-wheels. These in turn worked hands over the faces of dials, or caused figures to turn round, balls to be discharged, and even trumpets to sound. In some cases the fluid escaped from a urinating figure, in others it more modestly flowed as tears from the eyes of automata. In all cases the devices were unreliable, for changes in temperature, air-pressure, or size of orifice due to corrosion all affected the rate of liquid flow.

Like the Greeks, the Romans also used simple water-clocks in the senate house and courts of law. This custom supplied the witty first-century poet Martialis with a humorous allusion; he describes how one dull declaimer had to keep moistening his over-taxed throat with water, and suggests that if he had drunk from the clepsydra itself it would have benefited both the orator and his audience. Water-clocks were also employed at public baths, and they indicated the passing hours through the sound of a brazen gong or a trumpet. In their various forms they were introduced into Britain during the Roman occupation, although Caesar is said to have found a primitive type of water-clock already in use when he came to our shores in 55 B.C.

Mention of Julius Caesar reminds us of the two bright comets which appeared in 48 and 44 B.C. These unusual objects, like many previous and subsequent apparitions, were variously regarded as heralds of misfortune and auspicious omens. The times were sufficiently violent for augurs, diviners, and soothsayers to be pretty certain that a comet would herald some drastic change in the Government. The first visitor appeared during the civil war between Caesar and Pompey, and was regarded as a hairy and demoniacal messenger of the gods who were about to reshape the destinies of men by some dreadful upheaval. According to the Roman poet Lucan who wrote a century after the event, the darkest nights were made light by unknown stars, while burning torches traversed the heavens and made them appear on fire. Subsequent events certainly appeared to favour those who prophesied rivers of blood. On August 9, 48 B.C., Roman fought Roman at Pharsalia in Thessaly. With his legions defeated, Pompey fled to Egypt, but on landing and in full sight of his fifth wife, he was stabbed in the back. His head was cut off and shown to Caesar when he arrived in pursuit, but the victor turned away from the sight, shed tears of disconsolation, and had the murderers put to death.

Caesar met a similar fate at the foot of Pompey's statue on March 15, 44 B.C., after which dread event a comet is said to have waxed so bright that it became visible in daytime—and on the very day when Octavian performed the rites in honour of his dead great-uncle. To the multitude the comet was nothing less than the soul of Caesar on its way to heaven, whilst to the party of Octavian it indicated the displeasure of the gods that Brutus, Cassius, and the other assassins remained unpunished. To many the comet presaged further civil discord no less violent than that which had followed its predecessor four years earlier. Pliny writes that Augustus dedicated a temple to the comet and that the year which followed Caesar's death was one of almost continuous gloom. According to the poet Virgil, the sun 'veiled his face in dusky gloom. . . . Germany heard the clash of arms over all the sky; the Alps rocked with unwonted earthquakes. A mighty voice, too, was commonly heard through all the silent groves and spectres strangely pale were seen under the cloud of night; and the very cattle (Oh horrible!) spoke; rivers stopped their courses, the earth yawned wide; the mourning ivory weeps in the temples, and the brazen statues sweat.' To the poet, all these and other prodigies heralded the fresh disaster of civil war and the bloodshed at Philippi, where Octavian and Antony dealt the death-blow to the Republican party.

A refreshing departure from these uncritical and superstitious ideas was made by Seneca, conventional Stoic philosopher and adviser to Nero. Seneca was clearly attracted by the notion that comets might be celestial objects far above the sphere of the moon and yet subject to physical laws. They might even be periodic phenomena, in which case he thought it advisable to collect and inter-compare records of previous comets. This was precisely what Edmund Halley did in the eighteenth century when his calculations and study of previous records enabled him to predict the 1759 return of the comet since known as 'Halley's comet'. 'Some day', Seneca predicts, 'there will arise a man who will demonstrate in what regions of the heavens the Comets take their way; why they journey so far apart from the other planets; what their size, their nature.' The prediction was fulfilled 1,600 years later when Newton worked out the dynamical plan of the solar system on the basis of the inverse square law of gravitation.

Seneca comments on that human weakness which makes us blind to the beauty around us—when its very familiarity robs it of its grandeur. Instead, we crave for things which are new and unusual, and often quite regardless of their intrinsic merits. The views of some moderns with regard to 'flying saucers' indicates that the love of the marvellous is still with us; others find astronomy attractive only when it has strong infusions of interplanetary travel, and seem to think that the primary concern of astronomers is to ascertain the nature of the life on Mars. 'The whole choir of heavenly constellations under this immense vault,' says Seneca, 'whose beauty they diversify, fails to attract the attention of the multitude; but should anything extraordinary appear, all faces are turned towards the heavens. The sun has spectators only when he is eclipsed. The moon is observed only when she undergoes a similar crisis. . . . The same thing takes place in respect to comets. If one of these flaming bodies should appear of rare and unusual form, everyone is anxious to see what it is; all the rest are forgotten whilst everyone inquires concerning the new arrival; no one knows whether to admire or to tremble; for there are not wanting people who draw from thence grave prognostics and disseminate fears.'

Although Seneca once stated that comets were redeemed of their infamy when they appeared during the reign of Nero, he never completely freed himself from the belief that they caused violent changes in the weather. Of the comet that appeared in 62 he wrote: 'Everywhere there have been violent storms; in Achaia and Macedonia several towns have been overthrown by earthquakes.' He was also impressed by the ball of fire seen at the death of Caesar Augustus, and described it as flashing into sight and moving very rapidly, disappearing as it moved. In 64, when Nero was well on the road to infamy and Seneca, among others, feared for the safety of his life, another comet appeared. Tacitus, the historian and friend of Pliny, voices the more popular belief when he says that the comet was a kind of presage that Nero expiated with the blood of the illustrious. In 65, Nero ordered the death of

Seneca, who anticipated the sentence in the Roman fashion by opening veins in his arms and legs. The following January yet another comet appeared, which Josephus mentions as standing like a sword over the city of Jerusalem during its sufferings at the hands of Titus. This was Halley's comet, the reappearance of which at intervals of about seventy-six years was perhaps known to the sages of Palestine.

The word 'comet' means 'hairy'—a not inapt description when applied to some of these visitants to the night sky. The comet of 79 was apparently of this appearance, for when the ailing Vespasian saw his courtiers conversing about it in undertones he remarked that 'this hairy star does not concern me; it menaces rather the King of the Parthians, for he is hairy and I am bald'. According to another chronicler, numerous prodigies preceded the death of Vespasian, among them a comet which remained visible for 'a long time' and the opening of its own accord of the door of the tomb of Augustus.

Vespasian died in the summer of 79; two months later Mount Vesuvius, on the Bay of Naples, erupted and Pompeii and Herculaneum and surrounding villages were buried under ashes. Led by his scientific curiosity and desire to rescue some of the stranded victims, the Prefect of the Misenum fleet, Pliny the elder, himself became stranded and so perished by suffocation with the rest.

Pliny was a Roman of wide interests and immense mental energy. An important official by day, he spent his evenings and often early mornings in literary labours. Jealous of every spare minute, he kept a secretary in constant attendance either to read to him or write down dictated observations. Travels on official business and bath- and lunch-times were usually occasions for listening to the reading of a new book or for dictating notes and letters. In this way, and by gleaning information of some 20,000 topics from 2,000 volumes, Pliny wrote his great *Historia Naturalis*. Besides giving much miscellaneous information, the thirty-seven books of this encyclopaedic but indiscriminate work embrace almost the entire field of Roman activity in science and technology. It was written about the year 77, was dedicated to Titus, the son of Vespasian, and had a great influence on questing minds in the Middle Ages.

Although Pliny's concern in the *Historia Naturalis* is largely with terrestrial phenomena, he gives many items of astronomical interest. He believes without hesitation that the earth is spherical, if only because of the gradual appearance of ships as they approach the shore. The sphericity, he finds, is also indicated by the fact that if a pocket sundial is to give correct time, its style must be adjusted for inclination whenever the instrument is used more than about fifty miles north or south of its permanent home. Similarly, the time of day at which a lunar eclipse occurs is not the same for all places, being different by about a quarter of an hour for two observers separated by about 200 miles in the east-to-west direction. If the earth was flat, all observers would see the beginning and end of the eclipse simultaneously. But these subtleties were known only to the educated minority: 'The mob', Pliny writes, 'ask how men on the antipodes do not fall off; as though that did not present the opposite query, why they should not wonder at our falling off.'

In Pliny's time, belief in judicial astrology was growing, despite various decrees which aimed at curbing its practice. Under the Caesars, its devotees—'the Chaldeans', as they were appropriately called—gained a good if uneasy living, and often counted senators and even the emperor himself among their patrons. Tiberius for one, when he temporarily forsook public life in 6 B.C. and retired to Rhodes, gave special attention to the study of astrology. When he became emperor and took up his residence on the island of Capri, he hit upon the following method of eliminating those whose word he distrusted. The imperial rooms were located at the top of a lofty cliff reached by a long, narrow path, and a single push from the burly guide hurled the unsuspecting victim into the sea below. To this retreat came the astrologer Thrasyllus, and after he had stated the results of his art as they concerned the emperor, Tiberius asked him whether he could calculate how long he had to live. The astrologer consulted his tables, and with evident terror declared that the present hour was for him critical, perhaps even fatal. Tiberius thereupon told him that whilst his prediction was correct, the danger was already past, and he could consider himself not only safe but appointed imperial counsellor.

Astrology was then deemed the special prerogative of oriental seers, who in background and training were steeped in the mysteries and magical practices of the East. 'As for the branch of astronomy which concerns the influences of the twelve signs of the zodiac, the five planets, the sun, and the moon upon human life,' writes Vitruvius, 'we must leave it to the calculations of the Chaldeans to whom belongs the art of casting nativities, which enables them to declare the past and future by means of calculations based on the stars.' This was the general attitude among educated classes; astrology was a science which had 'something in it', as many still persist in believing today, but good practitioners seemed to be scarce, and even their findings were not always reliable. Cicero, for one, points out that whilst the Chaldeans predicted that Caesar, Crassus, and Pompey would die peaceably at a ripe old age, all three had deaths which were 'violent, immature, and tragical'. Although he wrote a dialogue against divination, Cicero accepted some of its doctrines but without being well-informed in its techniques. His attack was directed mainly against liver divination; what connection is there, he asks, between the liver of a fat bull and the divine rule of the universe? In his *Dream of Scipio* he speaks of Mars as being 'ruddy and awful' and Jupiter as being 'beneficent and propitious', yet elsewhere he asks, 'What contagion can reach us from the planets whose distance is almost infinite?'

Tacitus blamed false predictions on 'the ignorance of those who profess the art', and Seneca thought that the Chaldeans erred in not taking all the stars into account. The fixed stars are undoubtedly very distant, he admits, but they do not shine in vain and cannot be 'without rule and dominion over us'. He also believed in divination from thunder and considered thunderbolts were portents of the future.

Although Pliny does not show much faith in the bolder claims of astrologers, he is sufficiently credulous and a man of his times not to doubt the influences on nature ascribed to the heavenly bodies. Like Seneca, he believes in thunder divination and considers thunderbolts bear omens of the future and come from the planet Venus, a planet which otherwise rules over all animal fertility. Comets generally signify disaster. 'A comet', he observes, 'is ordinarily a very fearful star; it announces no small effusion of blood. We have seen an example of this during the civil commotion of the consulate of Octavius [86 B.C.].' What comets portend may be found by noting their directions, shapes, and positions relative to the signs of the zodiac, to assist in which Pliny classifies them into twelve varieties such as disk-, cask-, spear-, and sword-shaped.

By the time of Pliny astrologers had extended the moon's sway over most of animate nature. Just as it was known to cause the ebb and flow of the sea, so the moon was considered to preside over the flux of the blood and other humours in animals, and the rise of sap in plants. Agricultural activities like tree-felling, seed-sowing, and crop-gathering were believed to produce best results when conducted under the appropriate phase of the moon. The marvellous virtues of many herbs could be captured only by plucking them on the right day of the month and with due observance to appropriate rituals. Often the left hand was more effective than the right, suitable charms and prayers had to be uttered, and a state of virginity and even nudity was sometimes deemed essential. Foremost among herbs used for healing wounds was Moon-wort (*Botrychium Lunaria*), a small fern whose fleshy moon-shaped pinnae were thought to be impregnated with lunar vitality. For reasons of growth and the moon, the Druids cut the mistletoe with sickles, and the Emperor Tiberius is said to have had his hair cut only when the moon was on the wane.

The supposed lunar influence on animal juices naturally

dictated ideas about animal behaviour and the treatment of ailments and diseases. To appreciate these connections we have to remember that when Hippocrates and his disciples replaced supernatural forces by natural laws, medicine became burdened with fluids, principles, and spirits of a mystico-material nature. Ideas of vital spirits and of four humours entered medicine about the fifth century B.C. and remained, with modifications, until well into the eighteenth century. Living bodies were supposed to be composed of the four humours, blood, phlegm, yellow bile, and black bile. These in their Latinized forms are respectively sanguis, pituita, choler, and melancholia. A disturbance in the balance of these humours, or the presence of a humour too fulsome, too morbid or corrupt, constituted disease. Hence remedies aimed at restoring the *status quo* to the extent of purging away the morbid humour. To draw the latter away from an affected region, the eyes included, recourse was made to hot poultices, irritants, bleeding, cautery, and trephining of the skull. Alternatively, the humoral balance could be achieved by a re-balancing of the four principles hot, cold, moist, and dry. The Roman Aurelianus writes that the poison introduced by the bite of a mad dog 'is so hot and dry, that it consumes all the moisture in the body'. A common cure for hydrophobia was to duck sufferers in sea-water. On the basis that the moon affects the humoral balance, therefore, Galen, the great second-century surgeon and physician, taught that children born when the moon was sickle-shaped were likely to be weak and short-lived, whereas those born at the full moon were lusty and bore the promise of a long life. Pliny, who records some five hundred 'diseases', records that careful study has shown that diseases of the eyes of certain beasts of burden increase and decrease with the moon—also that the number of parts to the entrails of a mouse equals the number of days in a lunar month (taken presumably as 30 and not $29\frac{1}{2}$!).

As the moon waxed and waned, so lesser animals, like shellfish, sea-urchins, crabs, and tortoises, were supposed to swell and retract in monthly unison. A tortoise, says Pliny, is fattest on the

fifteenth day of the lunar month, and it should then be killed if
its fat is to be used as an ointment against a quartan fever. For
similar reasons the liver of a cat is most effective when prepared
and applied under a waning moon. The practice of periodical
phlebotomy or blood-letting was also justified on the basis that
the moon controls the quantity of blood and the balance of the
humours in the human body. 'In the first quadrant,' writes an
early chronicler, 'it is warm and damp, at which time it is good to
let the blood of sanguine persons; in its second it is warm and dry,
at which time it is good to bleed the choleric; in its third quadrant
it is cold and moist, and phlegmatic people may be bled; and in its
fourth it is cold and dry, at which time it is well to bleed the
melancholic.' Small wonder, therefore, that in the Middle Ages
astrology became closely linked with medical practice—that doc-
tors of physick, following Galen, considered the influence of the
moon in each sign of the zodiac and in relation to other planets
before prescribing treatment.

Connected with the supposed lunar influence upon blood supply and fertility was the belief that a menstruating woman possessed unusual magical powers. She could blast vines and ivy by
touching them, cause copper to tarnish, and make bees desert
their hives. In compensation, she could rid a field of pests, calm
storms at sea, and remedy barrenness.

At this stage it is worth noting that the moon itself is far from
being the cold, moist, watery, and phlegmatic planet of astrology.
Instead, it is waterless and airless, and on its surface hot to the
degree that lead would melt on the sunlit side. As we have already
seen, Anaxagoras came near to the truth when he taught that the
moon has plains and valleys. Another idea, due apparently to
Pythagoras and fostered by the shaded appearance of parts of the
moon's disk, likened the moon to a transparent crystal ball which
reflected sunlight and mirrored the seas of the earth. Some of the
Pythagoreans appear to have reverted to the ideas of Anaxagoras,
and believed that our satellite sustains both plants and animals.
Another suggestion was that the moon's surface is quite smooth,

the apparent markings on its face being due to defects in our vision. Pliny even wrote a book which he called *De Facie in Orbe Lunae*, or *On the Face in the Moon*, in which he discusses all these possibilities and decides in favour of a rough and variously marked lunar surface: 'as to this apparent face in her, let us suppose that, just as our earth has certain great depressions, so she is opened up by great depths and clefts containing water or dark air, which the light of the sun does not penetrate or touch, but is there eclipsed, so that the reflection sent hither is scattered'.

Pliny is correct when he suggests that the moon absorbs some of the sun's light and reflects or scatters the rest. The moon's surface reflects not a subtle emanation but sunshine, the amount of which is admittedly so low in energy content that we experience no heating effect. This being the case, moonlight can exercise no malefic or baneful influence upon the brain and eyes. The Scriptural promise that 'The sun shall not smite thee by day nor the moon by night' perhaps refers to so-called 'moon-blindness'. Pliny voices an aspect of this old belief when he writes that those who lie exposed to moonlight become drowsy and stupefied, although elsewhere he says that this procedure is sometimes adopted as part of the treatment for the speedy removal of warts.

Yet the idea that moonlight can cause blindness and even insanity is deeply rooted in medical lore, and the belief that lunatics are most violent at the times of full moon persists today. Perhaps a bright, moonlit night makes sleep more difficult—but the writer is in no position to comment with experience on this tentative explanation. Historically, however, the traditional connection between moonlight and lunacy seems to have sprung from the association of fertility with the lunar cycle. To become pregnant was to become possessed, to come under the full influence of the moon. In fourth-century China, for example, Taoist women indulged in sexual exercises and exposed themselves to the moon so that their bodies might absorb its animating and watery Yin principle. Furthermore, a protracted gaze on some sacred objects was believed to evoke frenzy, hysteria, or prophetic delirium—excesses then mistaken for inspiration. No less significant is the old idea that the brain, regarded by Aristotle as a cold and insensitive organ, is akin to a microcosmic moon—that it waxes and wanes in sympathy with a dominating lunar influence. It never seemed to occur to astrologers that the moon itself remains one and the same body regardless of phase, or that the phase is due solely to particular circumstances of illumination and perspective. The terms 'lunacy' and 'lunatic' perpetuate these old beliefs. Many astronomers have from time to time spent innumerable hours in the detailed examination of the moon's surface features through telescopes, but they do not seem to be any queerer than the rest of their colleagues. There is, as yet, no foundation for changing the old saying: 'The undevout astronomer is mad' to 'The lunar astronomer is mad.'

Despite the findings of physics and meteorology to the contrary, there is still a widespread belief that the moon influences the weather. Perhaps the knowledge that our satellite, although about 240,000 miles away, is largely responsible for the tides at sea, encourages some folk to reason that the ocean of air is likewise influenced to a marked degree. There *is* a lunar influence, but the atmospheric tides to which it gives rise are extremely feeble. They could not alone give rise to rain-belts or lead to appreciable meteorological changes—hence the influence of the moon on either climate or weather must be discounted. Yet most of us have at some time heard the expression 'dry moon' or 'wet moon', or have been told by some wiseacre that fine weather will follow when the moon appears on its back and holds all the rain like a giant basin.

In general then, the leaders of Roman thought accepted doses of magical lore which we would today class as nonsense, yet scorned the claims of non-judicial astrology with its horoscopes and nativities. It seemed incredible to them that a person's future could be predicted from the appearance of the heavens at the time of his birth, and that the whole course of his life on earth should then and there be irrevocably fixed by God. If these ideas were unattractive to men who embraced the determinism of the Stoic philosophy, they were entirely abhorrent to their successors, the Christian fathers. Augustine, Tertullian, Hippolytus, and Lactantius Firmianus of Gaul all inveighed mightily against this denial of human free will, dignity, and individual salvation. Life to them was not a case of passive resistance to a remorseless fate, but a battle against evil demons who constantly assail man in the hope of effecting his moral and spiritual ruin. The heavens, the noblest part of God's creation, knows no imperfection, and therefore its denizens can in no way harm mankind. Malefic influences from the heavenly bodies were thus made attributable to the activities of the much closer and no less powerful minions of the chained Lucifer. Thus Lactantius Firmianus believed that demons 'produce disease, dreams, madness, in order to fetter men more closely to themselves by terror'. 'The lunatics', Jerome emphasizes, 'were not really smitten by the moon, but were believed to be so, through the subtlety of the demons, who by observing the seasons of the moon sought to bring an evil report against the creation, that it might redound to the blasphemy of the Creator.' Even so, the planets could still be regarded as the mighty revealers of fate, although subservient to the one all-powerful God, and judicial astrology suffered little at the hands of Christian theology. Indeed, and as we shall see in Chapter IX, it finally emerged triumphant within the very portals of the Church itself.

CHAPTER VII

CIRCULAR ORBITS

When they come to model heaven
And calculate the stars, how they will wield
The mighty frame; how build, unbuild, contrive
To save appearances; how gird the sphere
With centric and eccentric scribbled o'er,
Cycle and epicycle, orb in orb.

John Milton

CLAUDIUS PTOLEMY, called Ptolemy, the only great astronomer of Roman times and the last important observer at Alexandria, worked there over the period A.D. 127 to 150. Although we do not know the precise dates of his birth and death, the period mentioned is definite since his first recorded observation, an eclipse of the moon, was made in the eleventh year of the reign of the Emperor Hadrian, that is, A.D. 127, and his last in A.D. 150. He was probably born in A.D. 70 at Pelusium on the north-eastern edge of the Nile Delta, is said to have outlived the Emperor Antoninus Pius, and was therefore alive in 161.

In those times the city was eminently prosperous and esteemed the first in the world after Rome. Egypt on the other hand, then considered as a vast granary and treasure-house, was being systematically exploited for its wealth and was well on the way to economic ruin. As Egypt's main port, Alexandria handled a vast export trade which ranged from grain to Egyptian jewellery and monuments. Culturally the city resembled a large crucible in which many faiths, ideologies and philosophies simmered at gentle heat but from which Christianity was slowly emerging triumphant. When Hadrian visited the city in 130 he found the cult of the money-god surpassed all others in popularity. 'There is not a Jewish ruler of a synagogue, nor a Samaritan, nor a Christian elder,' he wrote, 'who is not an astrologer, a soothsayer, or a quack. When the Jewish patriarch himself comes to Egypt, some of them make him worship Serapis, others Christ.'

Surrounded by a self-seeking and pleasure-loving society, Ptolemy found tranquillity and intellectual freedom in the Museum and library of the Serapeum. Here he read the texts and studied the star globe prepared by Hipparchus, and finding that no one had troubled to extend the Hipparchic planetary system or check the star positions, he decided to make astronomy his main life's work. 'I know that I am mortal and ephemeral,' he writes, 'but when I scan the multitudinous circling spirals of the stars, no longer do I touch Earth with my feet, but sit with Zeus himself, and take my fill of the ambrosial food of the gods.'

Ptolemy made a number of observations with graduated instruments of his own devising, but in general his practical findings were less accurate than those obtained by Hipparchus. This is the more remarkable (and regrettable) since after 300 years some of the errors made by Hipparchus had grown from minutes of arc into several degrees. It was also unfortunate that he gave 2 minutes 51 seconds as the value of the solar parallax, a measure of the sun's distance which was accepted without question by astronomers until well into the sixteenth century. The actual value is nearer only 8 seconds, which puts the sun some 93 million miles distant, but this value was not obtainable until after the invention of the telescope. Like Hipparchus, Ptolemy had a pretty good idea of the size and distance of the moon, but his values for the sun are about twenty times too small. He had, of course, no way of finding the distances of the planets—this was achieved much later by Copernicus. His remarkable skill and interest in geometry, however, enabled him to elaborate Hipparchus's planetary system (especially with regard to the motion of the moon) to a form which stood the tests of over 1,000 years. As he developed his system and exploited to the full the cherished idea of uniform motion in circular orbits, he became increasingly aware of its descriptive nature. For him, and undoubtedly for Hipparchus, the circles, epicycles, and deferents were abstract things. He must have often felt that the entire system was perhaps too remote from the customary physical view of nature. Yet as an aid to computation it admirably fulfilled its purpose, for it enabled him both to check earlier Greek and Babylonian observations of eclipses and the positions of the planets, and predict future eclipses and planetary appearances. In brief, the Ptolemaic system, with its fixed, central earth and eighty component circles, described the then known motions of the sun, moon, and planets as accurately as was possible with the methods available. It was at once a triumph of scientific inquiry and a masterpiece of geometrical ingenuity.

For Ptolemy the earth is a sphere fixed immovably in the centre of the heavens. In size it is but a point compared with the immensity of the cosmos, for from all parts of the earth the stars individually appear of the same brightness and retain the same relative positions. If it rotated, he argued, objects on its surface would be hurled off like mud from a spinning-wheel. Yet it never occurred to him that the sphere of fixed stars, being so much larger than the earth, would disrupt under its own angular velocity; early cosmological schemes were innocent of dynamical considerations!

As we shall see in successive chapters, the Ptolemaic system gained complete ascendancy over the mind of man for fourteen centuries. By the time of Copernicus in the sixteenth it was of an incredible complexity, for its fusion with the physical ideas of Aristotle and the discovery of new irregularities in the motions of the planets led respectively to mechanical absurdity and the addition of further epicycles. Small wonder that Alphonso X of Leon and Castille in the thirteenth century despaired of ever understanding its complicated machinery. He it was who once declared to an assembly of bishops that if the Deity had consulted him at the creation of the world, he would have advised the adoption of a less complex scheme.

In his survey of the stars Ptolemy was assisted by the catalogue of star positions drawn up by Hipparchus. He used forty-eight constellations, but with the qualification that 'we employ not the same Figures of the Constellations that those before us did, as neither did they of those before them, but frequently made use of others that more truly represent the Forms for which they are drawn'. Stars outside these groupings, or modifications of older groupings, he ignored, an omission which permitted the inclusion at later dates of new constellations like the Dove, the Sculptor, the Phoenix, and the Fox. In general, he was content to reduce the star positions of Hipparchus by applying a wrong value of the precession, and appears to have adopted Hipparchus's star magnitudes without making any revision. Altogether he catalogued 1,022 stars, both with respect to their positions in the appropriate constellation figures and in terms of celestial latitude and longitude. In the former case, and in common with other ancient writers, he described the figures as they might supposedly be seen from the outside of the celestial sphere. Modern maps and globes, it should be noted, show them as they might be seen in the sky, that is, as if drawn on the inside of a hollow globe. Like Aratus, but more extensively, he also recorded the appearance of several of the fifteen brightest stars seen from Alexandria. Thus Sirius is 'Seirios', 'the sparkling one'; Antares is 'the representative of Ares or Mars'; Arcturus, Aldebaran, and Betelgeuze are described as 'fire-coloured' stars. As will be seen in Chapter VIII, the majority of our present star names is of Arabic origin.

Ptolemy was the first to appreciate that the Milky Way is a phenomenon worthy of detailed description, and his account of its different parts reveals much careful observation. 'The Milky Way,' he writes, 'is not a circle, but a zone, which is almost everywhere as white as milk, and this has given it the name it bears. Now, this zone is neither equal nor regular everywhere, but varies as much in whiteness as in shade of colour, as well as in the number of stars in its parts, and by the diversity of its positions; and also because that in some places it is divided into two branches, as is easy to see if we examine it with a little attention.' He then describes its course across the heavens, showing where it appears 'rather dull' (in parts of the Ship Argo), and where 'dense' and 'like a smoke' (in the Archer). To his predecessors the Milky Way never seemed to warrant this attention—most Romans were content to regard it as the avenue of the gods. Aristotle, as we have seen, considered it to be a collection of exhalations from the stars; the Egyptians saw it as the celestial course of the river Nile. Aratus viewed it with a poetical eye:

> If with admiring ken some cloudless night,
> When no full moon obtrudes her jealous light,
> To the high Heavens thou lift the starry eye,
> A radiant girdle belts the azure sky—
> A pearly pavement softly bright it seems—
> Its silvery whiteness rivals Cynthia's beams—
> The Milky Zone. No other circle given
> Thus visible to mortal eyes in Heaven.

In Ptolemy's time and for long afterwards, the boundary between astronomy and astrology was never very clearly defined; to most people the value of astronomy lay in its astrological applications. Sharpen the accuracy of prediction in the heavens, it was argued, and straightway you improve the scope and accuracy of prediction in the terrestrial domain. As Ptolemy himself admitted, astrology fell far short of perfection owing to the incomplete state of astronomical science. Not only was the art frequently abused by impostors, but it was in comparative infancy, since much more had to be known about its general rules—and these could be formed only by collecting more observations. We should not condemn it because it sometimes fails, he argued, no more than we should condemn a physician who fails to cure us, or the art of navigation because shipwrecks were then all too frequent. If ignorant sailors were able to predict the weather by merely looking at the sky, how much more should a highly-trained astronomer learn from it with respect to its human influences.

These and other ideas concerned with the astrological art Ptolemy unfolded in his *Tetrabiblos Quadripartitum*. He discussed the powers of individual stars and the signs of the zodiac, the effects of the planets considered alone and in relation to the stars, and the rules for drawing up horoscopes. He even attempted, but without much success, to give a physical explanation for the powers of the planets. His underlying idea is that the planets are affected by the damp vapours from the earth in various degrees according to their proximity to the earth. They also interact one with another and with the earth, affecting the latter in different ways according to the distribution on each body of the four elemental principles, hot, cold, dry, and moist. The moon, for example, is cold and moist in its influence because it gets a lion's share of the earth's vapours. Yet it is near enough to the sun to share appreciably in the sun's heat, so that its effect on other bodies (the earth included) is to make them soft and putrescent. Fortunately the earth receives the heat and drying influence of the sun . . . and so on until we land in a wilderness of complexity, and certainly never attain physical equilibrium.

That Ptolemy could write in all seriousness a book of this nature has been at once a feather in the cap of astrologers and a source of regret to astronomers. For the first time astrology received the official sanction of one who, like Aristotle, towered as a mental colossus astride the ancient world. The book was written not because Ptolemy possessed a strange streak of mysticism or had a mental relapse but because he lived and worked when and where he did. Beliefs which nowadays appear to be the products of naïve credulity and misdirected effort make sense when we view them against the background of their age.

Ptolemy also wrote on geography, and in his famous *Geographia* developed Eratosthenes' cartography into a full latitude–longitude form analogous to the system used by Hipparchus for fixing star positions. He knew the latitudes of a number of places, but they were neither numerous enough nor all consistently accurate, and he had to rely largely on itineraries and travel records. Even so, his world-map (or the world-map attributed to him) was a great improvement upon the previous efforts by Eratosthenes,

Strabo, Pomponius Mela, Marinus of Tyre, and others. It stretches in longitude from Spain to an unknown land beyond India, and but for the portrayal of the Western Ocean (Atlantic) could form one continuous land strip. The Western Ocean is shown of narrow width and leads invitingly to Eastern Asia. In latitude the map stretches from Thule, placed in latitude 60° N. and perhaps the Orkneys, down to the supposed source of the Nile in the Mountains of the Moon below 10° S. Except for the Mediterranean region (and even here the extent in longitude is 62° instead of 42°), proportions and coastlines are not very good. Ceylon is shown larger than Spain, and the Indian Ocean appears as a vast land-enclosed sea of unfamiliar northern outline. For the first time, however, inhabited regions are not shown to be entirely surrounded by water. Africa, for instance, is assumed to continue below Ethiopia into unknown torrid regions where water boils away and men turn black. 'There can be no doubt,' writes Pliny, 'that the Ethiopians are scorched by their vicinity to the sun's heat, and that they are born like persons who have been burned, with beard and hair frizzled.' The Cape of Good Hope was not rounded until 1488, and then by Portuguese mariners under Bartholomew Diaz, who thus pointed the way to a sea route from Europe to India.

For tracing his coastlines, Ptolemy probably availed himself of the reports of merchants, travellers, ship-masters, and seamen; ships in those days before the magnetic compass and astrolabe (see pp. 141, 142) seldom left sight of the coast. It was also easy to err in estimating direction and even distance; Caesar, Pliny, and Tacitus, for instance, all believed that Spain lies well to the west of Britain, and although Ptolemy corrected this, he gave Scotland an east-to-west trend. Without doubt he also made use of Roman itineraries drawn up under the instructions of Caesar and continued by the diligent Vipsanius Agrippa, the son-in-law of the Emperor Augustus. From copies of these and similar military route-maps preserved at Alexandria he would learn something of the extent and shape of Britain, including Ireland, which Pomponius Mela informs us 'abounds in herbs of pleasant appearance and so sweet that the flocks fill themselves to repletion in a short part of the day, so that if not prevented from eating they would burst with fatness'.

Of the original Greek form of Ptolemy's work on optics we cannot form any complete estimate, for the original Greek text and the first of the five books are lost. The work is important since for the first time ideas about the eye and vision, reflection and mirrors, and the bending or refraction of light by water and glass are grouped together under one heading and discussed by the geometrical treatment of experimental findings. Both Euclid and Hero of Alexandria had investigated the optical properties of plane and curved mirrors, Euclid being responsible for the idea that light travels in straight lines in the form of rays, and for the first enunciation of the laws of reflection. Ptolemy shared his belief that when we see a thing it is because visual rays leave the eyes, strike the object being viewed, and are reflected back again into the eyes. They then so blended with the animal spirit or higher-type pneuma in the globes that appropriate images passed to the brain via the supposedly hollow optic nerves. Anomalies of vision were attributed to some defect in the pneuma—to it being weak, inflamed, or 'perverted'. Aristotle had dispensed with the issuing visual rays, but had made the heart the seat of sensation; Galen thought that the retina lined the back of the lens of the eye and hence acted as a mirror. Ptolemy reinstated the emergent rays and wrote of their geometrical behaviour—of the appreciation of distance and direction. This notion straightway invested light with immense speed, for although the stars are immeasurably distant, they can be seen during the flickering of the eyelids.

Ptolemy made no mention of Seneca's earlier observation that a glass globe filled with water can be used as a kind of magnifying glass for near objects. He was, however, the first to investigate the refraction of light; he invented a simple apparatus for measuring angles of incidence and refraction, and concluded that for any two given media like air and water, the angle of incidence in air is greater than the angle of refraction in water. The two angles, moreover, were found to be related in a constant ratio—a result which is regarded as being true today whenever very small angles are involved.

As we shall see in the following chapters, the science of optics was of slow growth, and the first spectacles did not appear until as late as about 1300. Hans Lippershey, a spectacle-maker of Middelburg in Holland, invented the telescope early in the seventeenth century, and its successful application to astronomy by Galileo focused more attention on optics. After the classic work of Newton, the founder of optics as a science, its practical aspects almost dictated the course and progress of astronomy. Every increase in the power, light-grasp, and optical excellence of telescopes, whether they were composed of mirrors or lenses, extended the boundaries of man's vision and understanding of the heavens. Discoveries followed as a matter of course.

Ptolemy naturally had no idea that optics would one day link forces with astronomy. For him the subject was merely a new and interesting aspect of geometry. If he made but small progress in this seemingly strange field, his book did at least point the way for future inquiries and invite men like Al-Hazen, Vitellio, Grosseteste, and Roger Bacon of later ages to penetrate further. We have also to remember that appearances seen in and produced by mirrors of various forms were generally regarded as being semimagical. Divination from polished surfaces was for many centuries regarded as one of the many ways of divining the future.

Ptolemy's preoccupation with astronomy and geography apparently gave him little opportunity for participating in the then growing interest in chemistry. This subject had arisen out of the fusion of aspects of Hellenistic philosophy with Egyptian magic and practical knowledge in glassmaking and metallurgy. Unfortunately, the philosophical ingredients contained so much mysticism and magic that rational chemistry was almost strangled at birth. Astrology exerted a considerable influence in this new field, for not only the planets but even their mythological symbols were believed to have a sympathetic connection with metals. The sun, or masculine principle, presided over gold, the moon, or feminine principle, over silver. Mercury had control over tin and Venus had control over copper. Iron, the metal of war, was associated with Mars, and electrum, an alloy of gold and silver, with Jupiter. Dull and heavy lead was the metal of slow-moving Saturn. This particular allocation of metals to the planets varied from time to time, but the basic notion of metal and planetary affinities, once implanted, dominated Alexandrian metallurgy and persisted for well over a thousand years. Thus for Chaucer, writing in the fourteenth century,

> Sol gold is, and Luna silver we threpe;
> Mars iren, Mercurie quicksilver we clepe:
> Saturnus led, and Jupiter is tin,
> And Venus coper, by my faderkin.

Just as a modern chemist attends to the control of weight, volume, temperature, and so on, the 'sons of Hermes' sought success through propitious influences, spirits, and demons. Hence the use of magic spells, incantations, quintessences, cabalistic signs, and mystic numbers became essential parts of chemical procedures. Occult properties were valued far more than physical appearances. Yet the latter were often the sole guides to transformations. For the early chemists a metal had only to change its colour through the addition of sulphur or mercury to become a new substance—to be transformed or transmuted into a completely new entity. For the Arabians, who added the prefix 'al' to 'Khem' and so gave us 'alchemy' (al-Khem = 'art of the dark country', i.e. Egypt), the universal transmuting agent was called an 'elixir'—the 'philosopher's stone' of the alchemists of the Middle Ages.

Reasons for this deep interest in the occult are not difficult to find. Early in the Christian era, and closely connected with Christianity, there had arisen a sect who professed superior knowledge or 'gnosis' through the revelations of oriental religions. Known as the Gnostics, these mystics peopled the heavens with a hierarchy of spirits, demons, angels, and potentates which were supposed to preside over both animate and inanimate nature, and whose powers could be enlisted through sacred formulae and mystic symbols. Another sect, later called the Neo-Platonists, exploited the mystical sublimities of Plato's teaching as interpreted by Ammonius Saccas, an apostate Christian, and his pupil Plotinus, an Egyptian occultist who taught in both Alexandria and Rome during the third century. Like Plato, Saccus and Plotinus believed that the stars and planets possess souls—that they are divinities harmoniously disposed one towards another, and influential in the terrestrial domain. These and other absurdities, infused with Babylonian astrology, were extended by Porphyry and Iamblichus, and applied to alchemy by Zosimus, Mary the Jewess, Marianus, and others.

Just as the Virgin Mary and the saints assumed for Christians the places left vacant by discarded pagan deities, so the early Church elevated the spirits of Plato's cosmos into ordered arrays of angelic beings. By the fourth and fifth centuries, and especially through the teaching of St Augustine, the Church had accepted many Neo-Platonic doctrines. There followed the writings of Proclus, a verbose philosopher of fifth-century Athens, and of Dionysius the Areopagite, who claimed to be the companion of St Paul and Timothy. Dionysius, however, was probably a Syrian monk, and lived during the fifth to sixth centuries. Through both these authors the cosmos received an elaborate theocratic interpretation. There thus evolved that fanciful cosmology with its throned Deity, light-drenched Paradise, and descending orders of angels, together with an uncritical acceptance of magic and divination which precluded the superstitious fancies of the Middle Ages.

With these spiritual infusions afoot, it is strange that the early Fathers made no attempt to depose the Olympian gods from the spheres of heaven. Christian constellation figures were suggested during and after the eighth century, and starting with the Venerable Bede, but the proposed changes aroused little to no general interest. Had this been otherwise we might now have twelve apostles for the signs of the zodiac, the Barque of St Peter for the Plough, and St Sepulchre for the chained Andromeda.

After the time of Ptolemy little astronomical work of any consequence was done at Alexandria. This was due in part to the rise of Christianity and also to the gradual collapse of the military might of the Roman Empire during the fourth and fifth centuries. Greek philosophers, regarded as agents of the Devil and as so many false prophets, were accused of both undermining the Faith and sapping the virility and moral fibre of Rome. Torn by the disputes and wranglings of religious and pseudo-religious orders, Alexandria became a city of strife and mob violence. Under such conditions the pagan community was harassed and victimized almost to the point of extinction. Many scholars and philosophers of the old schools fled to Syria and Greece. Simplicius, the famous commentator on Aristotle, joined six others on a long journey to Persia, but had to return after a few years, for even there Greek wisdom was held in little respect. From the pulpit Justin Martyr damned Greek philosophy as a devilish heresy and referred his hearers to the Prophets, whose learning, so said Clement of Alexandria, the Greeks had pirated and given out as their own. Another attitude, expressed with no less force by Tertullian, insisted that the teaching of Christ had rendered all further learning superfluous.

The Museum was still standing in the first half of the third century, but in 274 the Emperor Aurelian besieged the fugitive Firmus in Alexandria and with military efficiency reduced to rubble the Museum and palaces and tombs of the Ptolemies. In 296 the Emperor Diocletian is said to have issued an edict which required the collection and burning of the books of the Alexandrian alchemists. In 391 the Patriarch Theophilus carried out Theodosius's decree for the destruction of pagan monuments by inciting the mob to burn the Serapeum. Its loss and the subsequent erection of a Christian Church on the same site inflicted a mortal blow to the prestige of the Graeco-Egyptian divinities both at Alexandria and in Italy. Part of the library was pillaged, including

many of the 200,000 manuscripts collected by the kings of Perga-
mos and presented by Mark Antony to Cleopatra. A further section received damage in 415 during similar riots under Patriarch
Cyril. On this latter occasion the mob cruelly murdered the Neo-
Platonist and mathematician, Hypatia, who as one early chronicler
records, was 'eminently learned in the Mathematicks and Philosophy, which she publickly professed and taught, till by the
barbarous Christians, or Monsters rather, of Alexandria, out of
meer envy . . . she was most inhumanely murthered and torn to
pieces in the very Cathedral Church'.

Despite these and other violent measures the Hellenic tradition
was slow in dying, and small groups of philosophers continued to
reside and work at Alexandria and Athens until well into the sixth
century. The last major pagan stronghold fell in 529, when Jus-
tinian closed the Academy and Lyceum at Athens and caused
scholars to emigrate to Syria and even distant Persia.

Yet the early Church was Christian in faith and pagan in culture. According to many of the early Fathers, mathematics and
astronomy were unworthy of attention, since they had no direct
moral significance. 'To discuss the nature and position of the
earth', says Ambrose, 'does not help us in our hope of the life to
come.' Statements like this, however true in a theological sense,
had a paralysing effect on human inquiry, for they implied virtue
in ignorance. Some Fathers adopted Neo-Platonic ideas and
sought the mystical significance of the numbers mentioned in the
Scriptures, and especially in Revelation. Some, like the scholarly
Augustine and Basil, accepted the heathen idea of a spherical
earth, whereas the Roman biographer Plutarch considered it
wholly fanciful. Other Fathers agreed with Plutarch, especially
Lactantius Firmianus, who says: 'Can anyone possibly be so
stupid as to believe that there are men then called Antipodes who
walk with their feet up and their heads down? . . . That crops and
trees grow downwards? That rain, snow, and hail fall upward to
the earth?' Augustine might believe in a spherical earth, but even
he could not summon courage enough to accept the Antipodes. In

the first place, there is no scriptural reference to such people, and in the second, how would it be possible to preach the gospel to them when the impenetrable barrier of the ocean stood in the way? Far better to deny their existence altogether!

Although he borrowed freely from Neo-Platonism, Augustine tended to ignore Greek science on the basis that nothing should be accepted unless on the authority of the Scriptures. 'What concern is it to me', he writes, 'whether the heavens as a sphere enclose the earth in the middle of the world or overhang it on either side?' The Scriptures state that there are waters above the firmament—hence Saturn, for Augustine, is both the most distant and the coolest planet. Even more childish was the scheme proposed by the sixth-century Alexandrian traveller-monk, Cosmus Indicopleustes, who rejected the pagan idea of a spherical heavens and thought that the world was more appropriately modelled on the pattern of the Tabernacle. He also asks how the earth 'can hang suspended in the air and not fall'. In his world, like that of the ancient Egyptians, everything is confined within an immense rectangular box. Its base is the earth, with Jerusalem in the middle, its sides are vast mountains, and its lid forms the vault of heaven. Fortunately this highly individual and unhappy 'Christian' cosmology had little appeal and soon fell into oblivion.

CHAPTER VIII

MUSLIM TORCHBEARERS

Did we not possess the books of the ancients in which their wonderful wisdom is immortalized and in which the manifold lessons of history are so dealt with that the past lives before our eyes, did we not have access to the riches of their experience which would otherwise have been barred to us, our share in Wisdom would be immeasurably smaller and our means of attaining a true perspective most meagre.

Al-Jahiz of Basra

EARLY in the seventh century mighty forces began to stir in the then little-known and culturally insignificant country of Arabia. Far south in the peninsula, in the land of Saba, the modern Yemen, there lived a people who from earliest times had contacts with Mesopotamia, Egypt, and Persia. Long before the Christian era the Sabaeans maintained a theocratic state, built large temples, and worshipped the Babylonian triad Sin, Shamash, and Ishtar. Their capital was Maryab or Ma'rib, where about 750 B.C. they constructed a great dam and undertook an extensive system of irrigation. They were builders, traders, and agriculturalists—a peaceful community, who, thanks to their comparative geographical isolation, escaped both Greek and Roman domination.

By the late sixth century A.D. we find Yemen and the more northerly province of Hejaz under the yoke of a somewhat loose Persian suzerainty and tormented by feuds between quarrelsome sects of Jews and Christians. Into this disturbed setting, and probably between 570 and 580 at Mecca in southern Hejaz, the prophet Mohammed was born. In his youth he came into contact with the

I   123

foreign civilization and religions which permeated his country, and soon felt the need for a complete reform of Arabian society. As he grew older, like so many religious mystics, he used to fall into trance-like states, during which he heard oracular and ecstatic utterances which he attributed to the Angel Gabriel. In 610 he collected 6,000 of these sayings in one work—the Qur'an (Koran) or Mohammedan Bible. Furthermore, he claimed to be at once the political leader of Arabia and the spiritual guide of a new religious movement which he called *Islam*. By the time of his death in 632, and starting from Medina, he had established autocratic rule over all Arabia, and sown the seeds of a vigorously puritanical and militant faith.

Mohammed taught that all mankind should be summoned to accept Islam. If any rejected the new faith, pagans in particular, they were to be exterminated. Jews and Christians were allowed the happy alternative of paying tribute; if they became converts they were allowed the same rights and privileges as the conquerors themselves. With fanatical zeal, and inspired by the words of the Koran, but with a wordly eye on the wealth ahead, the followers of Mohammed swept out of their inhospitable peninsula of deserts and scattered water-courses. They overran Syria, Egypt, and Persia with incredible speed. Alexandria fell in September 642, after a year's siege, and the comparatively small contents of the Serapeum library were either burnt or taken away. To the north, as in Egypt, the professional armies of the Byzantine Empire were no match for the tidal wave, which by 670 had flooded Asia Minor and was lapping the outer defences of the citadel of Constantinople. By 732 the new empire stretched from the River Oxus below the Aral Sea to north of the Pyrenees, where but for the firm stand made by Charles Martel and the Christians at Poitiers, it might have embraced the entire Mediterranean.

At Damascus, the first Islamic capital in the East, the Omayyad caliphs and their followers settled down to rule the eastern part of their newly-acquired empire. From the start they regarded themselves as patrons of learning, to further which they built and

equipped an observatory and began to collect the salvaged knowledge of Rome, Greece, Syria, and the Near East. At Damascus,
Antioch, Edessa and other centres, Christian Greeks, and Christian and Nestorian Jews * translated pagan texts on medicine,
mathematics, and astronomy. Through their efforts the treasures
of Hellenistic culture were tapped and for the next 200 years
coursed through the Mohammedan world in Arabic dress. In 755,
and after recurrent internal strife over rights of succession, the
political and cultural centre of eastern Islam was moved from
Syria into Babylonia. In 762 al-Mansur, the second ruler of the
new Abbasid caliphacy, established his Court at Baghdad.

Baghdad, then a new city, stood on the west bank of the Tigris
near the ruins of the old Sassanid capital of Ctesiphon. Whereas
Damascus drew largely from the heritage of Byzantium, Baghdad
came more under old oriental influences. Syria, Egypt, Greece,
Persia, and even distant India (with Chinese contacts) came to
have representatives there. In 773, for instance, a learned Hindu
named Mankah presented al-Mansur with a set of mathematical
and astronomical tables (the *Siddhanta*) by the aid of which it was
possible roughly to predict eclipses and the positions of the
planets. The caliph thereupon commissioned the Persian astronomer al-Fazari and his son to translate the work into Arabic. No
doubt he also asked for and received further Indian texts. At any
rate, the Arabians came into contact with Hindu numerals about
this time, together with the use of zero as a symbol to denote the
absence of a number or of certain powers of ten in a number.
Hitherto they had written numbers in words, and although they
modified the numerals to fit in with the letters of their alphabet,
the new symbolism became indispensable in commercial com-
putations. The Arabians were great traders, especially in the
Mediterranean region, and doubtless Hindu methods of numeration were passed on to the merchants of Italy and Asia Minor.

* Nestorians. A Christian sect founded in 428 by Nestorius, patriarch of Constantinople. Condemned as heretical in 431 by the Council of Ephesus, the Nestorians emigrated
to Syria and Persia.

Al-Mansur and his successors had an eye for the practical applications of science, and although they tolerated astrology, they never became its dupes. Thus the Persian astrologer Naubakht had to assist in the planning and organization of the building of central Baghdad, and see to it that the city had appropriate mosques, public buildings, baths, and an adequate sanitation system. Al-Mansur, in particular, was not a ruler who suffered fools gladly—his headsman was kept in regular employment. He also had a reputation for niggardliness and kept a keen eye on his revenues. During his reign his troops captured some Chinese paper-makers who were induced to teach their craft in Baghdad and Samarcand. Hitherto the Moslems had written on parchment and Egyptian papyrus; al-Mansur ordered his storekeepers to sell their large stock of papyrus, declaring that henceforth Baghdad would rely on home-produced paper.

Under Harun al-Rashid, the son of al-Mansur and the fourth caliph, the work of translation continued with even greater zest if not with greater accuracy, and an increasing number and variety of Greek texts were translated into both Syriac and Arabic. Al-Rashid, of course, is the hero and despotic caliph of the fabulous *Arabian Nights*, although he is seen in a more human role as the first caliph to play the Persian game of polo. Among the texts translated was Euclid's *Elements*, Ptolemy's *Syntax*, which became known in Arabic as the *Almagest*, and further medical works by Hippocrates and Galen. These tasks called for proficiency in the Greek language and also in medicine, mathematics, and astronomy, but at this period and for long afterwards these three subjects were closely linked. Scholars generally studied all three in order to become proficient in any one.

The Banu Musa, known as 'the Three Brothers', are said to have spent the greater part of their fortune (their father was a brigand of Khorasan) on the acquisition and translation of Greek manuscripts. Through their liberality the Nestorian physician and philologist Hunayn ibn Ishak was invited to Baghdad from the medical college at Jundishapur in south-west Persia. Although weak in mathematics, Hunayn made a start on the translation of Ptolemy's *Syntax*, but was more at home with the medical texts of Hippocrates and Galen. He also wrote a number of original works of his own, among them the earliest known textbook on vision and the anatomy of the eye. Such was his enthusiasm for his work that in attempts to trace a text of Galen's he travelled in Mesopotamia, Syria, Palestine, and Egypt, and visited Alexandria. 'Yet I was not able', he writes, 'to find aught save about half of it at Damascus.'

Aided by a large number of clerks and assistant scholars, Ishak's son, Ishak ibn Hunayn, continued the translation of the *Syntax*. All this activity was assisted by the growing supply of paper, for a paper-mill, the second of its type in Islam (since one was already in operation at Samarcand), was set up at Baghdad in 793.

Harun al-Raschid had interesting contacts with Western Europe when he corresponded with Charles the Great, or Charlemagne. This energetic monarch had a great thirst for knowledge and went to immense pains to ensure that others shared its benefits. Through the services of the learned Alcuin of York and others, he not only made his palace at Ingelheim a centre of learning but also set about organizing cathedral and monastery schools throughout his kingdom. It was probably at Ingelheim in 807 that Charlemagne received greetings from his oriental counterpart, together with numerous treasures, an elephant, and an elaborate brass water-clock. This clock is of interest since it presented the first rudiments of a striking-clock. As the water level fell it successively actuated twelve little doors arranged round a dial to indicate the hours. At each hour a door opened and discharged an appropriate number of small balls which fell one by one on to a brass bell or bells and disturbed every scholar within earshot. Apart from the striking of the bell, the hour of day could also be seen by noting the number of doors that were open. At twelve o'clock twelve little knights appeared, marched round the dial, and shut all the doors. This Arabian clock was apparently the first sounding clock ever to be installed in a European seat of learning.

The scholarly al-Mamun, the seventh and perhaps the greatest Abbasid caliph, was appropriately called the Charlemagne of the East. He welcomed men of learning to his court, sent a deputation to the Roman Emperor Leo at Byzantium with a request for Greek manuscripts, and housed the then large company of translators and immense library in an academy known as Baitu'l-Hikma, or *The House of Wisdom*. This he placed under the direction of the Nestorian physician Yahyah ibn Masawaih—a further indication of the high social and cultural status then accorded to those expert in physic. During this caliphacy important texts by Aristotle were translated.

Associated with *The House of Wisdom* was an observatory, founded in 829 and furnished with a variety of large graduated sighting instruments of the Greek type for measuring the altitudes and relative angular separations of stars, and the positions of the sun, moon, and planets. The great mathematician al-Khwarizmi observed both here and at Damascus, for he was commissioned to check, and if necessary to revise, some of Ptolemy's findings. As a young man he accompanied a mission to Afghanistan and probably returned through India. Back in Baghdad he became librarian at the academy, made a study of the Indian *Siddhanta*, and prepared astronomical and trigonometrical tables. He also wrote on algebra, or what was then called 'Al-gebr we'l mukabala', that is, 'the science of restoration and reduction'.

This important work, the basis of subsequent Arabic and medieval texts, contained a mixture of Arabic, Greek, and Indian ideas. The idea of applying certain arithmetical notions to equations seems largely to have been al-Khwarizmi's own. Greek influence, possibly that of Diophantus the Alexandrian, is seen in his geometrical illustrations and discussions of roots, whilst Hindu numerals accompany the illustrations and annotate the text. The latter, however, is wholly rhetorical in character—that is to say, the solution of equations is written in words and without the merest suggestion of the symbolism of today. For al-Khwarizmi, algebra and arithmetic were co-joint mathematical disciplines which served practical ends and needs. Yet in the problems of both he must be given full credit for introducing the Arabic–Hindu number-names.

Al-Khwarizmi seems to have been in charge of a large geographical survey which al-Mamun initiated and which required the united labours of some seventy assistants. Ptolemy's *Geography* was apparently translated about this time, and Arabian geographers followed his example of dividing the inhabited world into seven zones or climates. They showed little interest in countries outside their empire, however, and the map or 'image of the earth' which accompanied the final al-Mamun text is now lost. Presumably it contained little more than a coastal outline based on the Ptolemaic latitude–longitude system. The determination of the latitudes of important places, whether by measuring the altitude of the Pole Star or the meridian altitude of the sun (supplemented by reference to adequate solar tables), nevertheless helped to keep observational astronomy alive.

Another part of al-Mamun's geographic survey was to determine the length of a degree of the meridian, multiply it by 360, and so obtain the measure of the circumference of the earth. The observations were made on the plains of Tadmor in Syria, and Sinjar by the Red Sea, and consisted in sending observers both northwards and southwards from a chosen point until they saw the Pole Star respectively rise or sink one degree. They then measured the distance they had travelled and took the mean of the two results. Both al-Khwarizmi and the instrument-maker al-Asturlabi collaborated in the work, which led to the excessive value of 6,500 miles for the diameter of the earth.

Al-Khwarizmi drew much from Hindu astronomy and reckoned his longitudes from the meridian of Ujjiyaini,* a town in central India. This choice was doubtless dictated by the Hindu belief that the earth is somewhat pear-shaped, and that the highest point from the centre, the 'world summit', was on the meridian of Ujjiyaini.

* In the eighteenth century the great masonry instruments of Jay Singh's observatory at Ujjiyaini were the pride of Indian astronomy.

Al-Khwarizmi also tried his hand at calendar reform, but his suggested introduction of a solar year of 365 days into time-keeping failed to become accepted. The Mohammedan calendar, in accordance with teaching in the Koran, has always been strictly lunar and operates with twelve alternate months of 30 and 29 days to form a normal year of 354 days. Al-Khwarizmi furthermore suggested that the new year started with the time of the vernal equinox, that is, on March 21. This change was also at variance with religious ideas, for the Mohammedan era was reckoned from the first new moon after the Prophet's flight from Mecca to Medina—that is, from Friday, July 16, 622.

Astrology during this period was well represented by the writings of the erudite al-Kindi, a Neo-Platonic philosopher who was born about 850 at Kufa on the western branch of the Euphrates. According to him the stars and planets influence affairs on the earth because they radiate an occult influence in the form of rays. Similar rays are emitted by terrestrial objects, and even by the human body—the rays of the mind. Human life and behaviour is therefore conditioned by the manifold interactions of occult rays. These and similar ideas which so blended science with superstition that only a tangle of nonsense remained, had a profound effect on credulous minds in the Middle Ages.

About this time also (860), al-Farghani (called Alfraganus in the western world) composed a compendium or treatise on astronomy, which, although based on the Hunayns' translation of the *Syntax*, was the first comprehensive Arabic book on the subject. Besides giving tables of the motion of the sun and moon, al-Farghani adopted the Arabian idea of dividing the zone of the sky covered by the passage of the moon into twenty-eight equal parts. These 'Mansions of the Moon', as they were called, were akin to the signs of the zodiac, and although none of the moon's periods correspond to twenty-eight days, the Mansions were deemed important in both astrology and the Mohammedan calendar. Al-Farghani gave a full account of the calendars used by different nations, and gave the improved value of 23°

35' for the obliquity of the ecliptic against Ptolemy's value of 23° 51'.

In the belief that the mathematical constructions of the Ptolemaic system required a material dress, al-Farghani and his successors decked them out with the most unsuitable physical notions. In the first place, the great deferent circles were assumed to be the equators of solid crystalline spheres; the epicycles were smaller spheres made of the same transparent material and had the planets attached to their respective equators. In the second place, and owing to the 'horror vacui', or ancient dislike of having empty spaces between the planets, it was assumed that the greatest distance of each planet from the earth was equal to the least distance of the next planet above it. In brief, the cosmos was not unlike a vast crystalline onion, but purest in its outer layers and in a state of rapid rotation. This idea of a completely filled universe was an old idea, and was mentioned by Proclus as being fairly common in his time. Al-Farghani, however, used it to work out the relative dimensions of the spheres of the planets, and he incorporated the pseudo results in what became to be regarded as the typical Arabian view of the universe. These quite fallacious ideas, derived from a dynamically impossible cosmos, led him to imagine that the entire planetary system could be encompassed by a sphere of radius no greater than 12,000 times the radius of the earth.

Debased in this way the Ptolemaic model became partly reconciled with the system of Aristotle, except that in the former the planetary orbits are not concentric. Nevertheless, and owing largely to the popularity of al-Farghani's book and other Arabic texts of similar nature, this fused form of the two great Greek world-systems passed on into the western world.

Al-Mamun was nicknamed 'the commander of the unbelievers' because almost every kind of sect and heresy found representation at his court. Thus we are not surprised to find that two other important astronomers at Baghdad were both members of a mystic sect of Syrio-Babylonian star worshippers which had its centre at the ancient city of Harran in Chaldea. The sect seems to have offered prayers and sacrifices to the planets which were regarded as divinities; special importance was given to the practice of astrology, and the various conjunctions and oppositions of the planets were celebrated with festivals.

The star-worshipper al-Battani, known later by the Latinized name of Albategnius, was a Syrian prince. He observed from the palace of Rakkah to the north-west of Baghdad and also from Antioch. At both places he tested many of Ptolemy's findings by making further observations, especially with regard to the length of the solar year and the constants of the sun's (geocentric) orbit. He also determined the annual rate of precession with greater accuracy than had Ptolemy (1° in sixty-six instead of in 100 years), drew up a new set of astronomical tables, and incorporated his new discoveries in the *Science of the Stars*, a treatise on astronomy which eventually rivalled al-Farghani's text in popularity. Thabit ben Qurra, his elder contemporary and brother in the Sabaean sect, was born at Harran in 836. He, too, seems to have had some trouble with the elders there, and was finally forced to leave the district. At Baghdad he became one of al-Mamun's astronomers and founded a Sabaean order more to his own liking.

Thabit ben Qurra (or Korra) was a man of vast erudition and an accomplished linguist and mathematician. His numerous religious writings tell of rules of purity and impurity for animals chosen for sacrifice to the planets, various rituals for ensuring the efficacy of images and talismans, and the necessary procedures and times for performing magic and saying prayers. As a translator and mathematician he made fresh and greatly improved copies of the *Elements*, *Syntax*, and important mathematical works by Apollonius and Archimedes. He it was who paused from his deep but not too successful study of the *Elements* to write with evident rapture: 'We are the heirs and offspring of paganism which has spread gloriously over the world. Happy is he who for the sake of paganism bears his burden without growing weary.'

Thabit ben Qurra acquired doubtful celebrity through his resurrection of the idea of trepidation, a supposed variation in the amount and direction of precession which was introduced some time after Hipparchus and before Ptolemy. Thabit knew that Ptolemy's value of 36 minutes for the annual precession of the equinoxes was too small by 14 minutes, and this fact no doubt added weight to the idea. The full variation was thought to be imposed on the otherwise uniformly progressive motion, and to take the form of an oscillation of some 8° extent. This quite illusory effect not only required the addition of another crystal sphere (the ninth) outside that of the fixed stars, but it disfigured the majority of subsequent astronomical tables right up to the time of Tycho Brahe (sixteenth century).

Persian influence had always been strong at Baghdad, and in 945 it succeeded in overthrowing the then feeble Abbasid caliphacy. The new masters of the city and surrounding provinces were the Buwayhid princes of Mosul and western Persia. Under their rule the caliphs became mere puppets, for all secular authority and sovereignty was vested in the Buwayhid sultans. The latter were extravagant and fond of pleasure, but they nevertheless kept the interest in astronomy alive. During the early years of their rule they created new centres of observational activity at centres like Bokhara (the capital of Khorasan), Samarcand (north of modern Afghanistan), and Khiva (at the mouth of the Oxus and the birthplace of al-Khwarizmi). By this time (tenth to eleventh century) most of the available Greek texts of importance, together with many of lesser value, had been translated. Closer contacts were made with India, and at Ray or Rhages in northern Persia the Soldjuk sultans patronized practical work in astronomy and mathematics.

About the year 1000 we find al-Biruni, a Persian scholar, astronomer, physician, and traveller, settling at Ghaza in Afghanistan to write his first-hand study of the religion, customs, and history of the Hindus. He also wrote on Hindu numerals and the prehistoric formation of the Indus valley, discussed the rotation and size of the earth, determined the specific gravities of many precious stones and minerals, and estimated the latitudes and longitudes of important cities met with during his travels. Another late tenth-century Persian, Abu'l Wefa, wrote an immense treatise on astronomy which he optimistically called the *Almagest*, constructed tables of tangents and cotangents, and apparently discovered an irregularity of the moon's motion now known as the *variation* (see p. 215). At Ray, and under the enlightened sultan Malik Shah Jalal-al-Din, the poet Omar Khayyam worked at algebra and calendar reform. In the latter connection he brought the old Persian calendar to a degree of perfection which the historian Gibbon says 'surpasses the Julian and approaches the accuracy of the Gregorian style'. The calendar operated from March 16, 1079, but was unfortunately short-lived and nothing is now known of its details.

When the Arabians and Persians translated Ptolemy's *Syntax* they came across the Greek names which identified some of the brighter stars. Aratus, for instance, had named the seven brightest stars of the Pleiades and had recorded the names Arctouros (*Arcturus*), Aix (*Capella*), Protrygetor (*Epsilon Virginis*), Prokuon (*Procyon*), and Seirios (*Sirius*). Eratosthenes added *Canopus*, a star just visible from Rhodes but not from Greece, and also Stachys—'an ear of corn' and the Latin *Spica*. Among the Latin names we find *Polaris*, *Capella*, *Castor*, *Pollux*, *Bellatrix*, and *Regulus*. The Arabians then rendered all these into Arabic, at the same time giving names to most of the stars down to the third magnitude. Many of these star names, in modified and contracted forms, are still used today.

The most prominent early writer in this interesting side-line of astronomy was undoubtedly al-Sufi, a Persian astronomer from Ray who died in 986. He worked under the Buwayhid ruler Adhad-al-Davlat at Schiraz and Baghdad, wrote on astrology, and undertook geodetic measurements. His *Description of the Fixed Stars*, with its lists of star names, star brightnesses, and constellation figures, is generally considered to be one of the finest masterpieces of Muslim astronomy. In it he mentions the great nebula in Andromeda (first noticed in Europe by Simon Marius in 1612), and records his own brightness estimates of 1018 of Ptolemy's stars. 'Many people believe,' he writes, 'that the total number of fixed stars is 1025, but this is an evident error. The ancients [Hipparchus and Ptolemy] observed only this number of stars, which they divided into six classes according to magnitude. They placed the brightest in the first magnitude; those which are a little smaller in the second; those which are a little smaller again in the third; and so on to the sixth. As to those which are below the sixth magnitude, they found that their number was too great to count; and that is why they have omitted them.' Al-Sufi adopted this magnitude framework (which with refinements is in use today), made his estimates to a third of a magnitude, and generally proved to be a most careful and accurate observer.

For al-Sufi, and to give only a few examples, the bright star *Rigel* at the base of Orion is 'ridjl-al-djauza', which means 'the leg of the giant'; *Betelgeuze*, the reddish star at the top of the trapezium, is 'mankib-al-djauza' or 'the shoulder of the giant'; *Vega* of the Lyre is 'al-nasr al-vaki' or 'the falling eagle'. *Polaris*, the Pole Star, appears as 'al-rukkabah', 'the Charioteer', but other names are more akin to those used today—thus 'al-nasr al-tair' or 'the flying vulture'; 'al-dabaran' or 'the attendant'; 'al-gul' or 'the demon'; and 'fum-al-haut' or 'the mouth of the southern fish'. All these are sufficiently well-known to require no further comment. The names give a charm and interest to the constellation figures which to modern minds has almost vanished. The romance and utility of astronomy now lie in other and far more significant directions, so that its devotees are content to leave star names and constellation figures to scholars and historians.

In 969, the dynasty of Fatimid caliphs, carried forward by a great wave of social unrest and unorthodoxy, swept triumphant into Egypt. From their magnificent citadel in the new city of Cairo they rapidly extended their sway into Palestine and Syria—even, in 1056, temporarily seizing the reigns of power at Baghdad. Thus it transpired that the sciences were once again encouraged in the Lower Nile, but at Cairo instead of Alexandria, and by the Fatimids instead of the Ptolemies. In astronomy the most outstanding work at the new centre was done by Ibn Yunis, who worked around the period 829 to 1004, and mainly under the patronage of Caliph Hakem. Ibn Yunis had his observatory on the hill of Mokatim, near Cairo and overlooking the Nile valley and the distant pyramids of Gizeh. Here he recorded his own observations and those obtained by earlier observers. His main work, the *Hakemite Tables*, thus contained lists of positions of the sun and moon, eclipse records in some detail from 829 onwards, and observations concerned with the equinoxes, solstices, and the obliquity of the ecliptic.

Caliph Hakem also patronized al-Hazen who wrote on astronomy, astrology, geometry, and optics. Al-Hazen was born at Basra in southern Iraq and appears to have been trained as a physician. In the service of Caliph Hakem he undertook, but without success, to find methods for regulating the annual flooding of the Nile. The caliph thereupon decreed that al-Hazen must die, a fate which the unfortunate scholar escaped by feigning madness until the year 1020, when the caliph died. If this story is true, al-Hazen could hardly have taken advantage of the facilities and texts at the *House of Science* which the caliph founded at Cairo in 995. Nevertheless, during the last ten years of his life he studied and wrote extensively, commented on the optical work of Euclid and Ptolemy, and made a number of experiments with mirrors and lenses. Like al-Biruni, but apparently quite independently, he considered that vision was caused by light entering the eye in the first place—that 'the form of the perceived object passes into the eye and is transmuted by its transparent body'. He investigated afresh the effects produced by curved mirrors, and drew attention for the first time to the rôle of refraction in the magnifying effects of glass segments and glass globes filled with water. More important from the viewpoint of astronomy was the attention he drew to atmospheric refraction. He suggested, for example, that light is bent or refracted when it passes through the earth's atmosphere and that owing to this all stars except those directly overhead are seen slightly above their true places. This effect, he plainly saw, was greatest for stars near the horizon, and on this count he correctly explained the somewhat oval shape assumed by the sun when it rises and sets. This discovery, however, was in too much of a backwater to attract much attention, and it was not until after the time of Tycho Brahe that astronomers began systematically to correct their observations for the effects of atmospheric refraction.

During the twelfth century astronomy seems to have languished at Baghdad, owing largely to the then degenerate and politically weak state of the Abbasid caliphate under the Buwayhid sultans. Especially ominous were the growing forces of disruption both within and without the eastern empire. From Egypt, through Syria, and even in Asia Minor there extended the dreaded network of the Assassins, a fanatical sect founded in 1090 by Hassan ben Sabbah, the original 'Old Man of the Mountains' mentioned by the Crusaders. From his mountain retreat at Alamut, and surrounded by a picked gang of thugs, Hassan ben Sabbah pored over secret writings, astrological signs, and alchemical apparatus, terrorized the country round about and undermined still further the crumbling fortunes of the Abbasids. But a far greater threat loomed in eastern Asia, where the previously nomadic tribes of Mongolia became united under the leadership of the mighty Jenghiz Khan. In 1220 the court at Baghdad heard with concern that the Mongols had conquered Khorasan and Transoxiana, and devastated the ancient city of Ray, the birthplace of al-Sufi, centre of astronomical activity, and noted for its fine ceramic industry. Concern turned to alarm when in the following year Jenghiz crossed the Oxus and made a destructive raid deep into northern Persia. Events then moved more slowly, but in 1256 the Mongolian forces under Hulagu, grandson of the Great Khan, engulfed Persia and turned southwards into Mesopotamia.

Halted before Baghdad in 1258, Hulagu consulted his astrologer for favourable omens, but the pious Moslem prophesied six terrible misfortunes should the Mongols attack the city. Hulagu straightway ignored the celestial council of his seer, had him beheaded, and appointed a successor who unhesitatingly prophesied complete success. The army of the caliph was routed, and when the city suburbs were stormed three weeks later, the caliph surrendered unconditionally. For six days and nights the city was laid open to terrible massacre, pillage, and destruction; mosques were burnt, and the famous Mustansiriyah university, founded in 1234 for the study of law and the finest of its kind in the world, was left a shambles. Yet amidst all the strife and carnage one man at least had a set constructive purpose. He was Nasir ed-Din al-Tusi, and he and his slaves successfully cleared *The House of Wisdom* of its manuscripts.

Nasir ed-Din, born in 1200 at Tus in Khorasan near the modern Meshed, was for a time associated with the Assassins, although against his will. He was apparently rescued from their clutches, joined the service of Hulagu, and for three years watched ineffectual attempts to dislodge the hated raiders from their mountain fortress. In 1256, and under pressure from famine, the last remaining Assassin stronghold fell.

Leaving Baghdad largely in ruins, and after massacring some 800,000 inhabitants, including the caliph and his family, the Mongol leaders separated. Some swept on to extend the conquest towards Egypt and into Syria. Others returned to consolidate their gains in Persia, where they linked up with the new dynasty of the Ilkhans at capitals at Maragha, Tabriz, and Sultaniya. With them went Nasir ed-Din and the salvaged library, said to have once contained half a million texts. He became Hulagu's confidant and adviser, and in 1260 we find him newly-installed, with assistants and in charge of instruments of immense size, in a splendid new observatory at Maragha. Here he achieved a great reputation in the East for his great knowledge and attainments, although a late contemporary of his suggests that this could scarcely have been otherwise in view of Nasir ed-Din's violent temper, impatience of contradiction, and high power at the court of Hulagu. Yet the Persian is now recognized as having been a great astronomer and a man of broad culture. He prepared treatises on mathematics, and for the first time developed trigonometry independently of astronomy. In the latter subject he concerned himself with calendar reform and the compilation and publication of the tables and star catalogue in the *Il-khanic Tables* of 1269.

The last Persian stronghold of astronomy was at Samarcand, where another Mongol Emperor, Timur Leng or Tamerlane, ruled his vast empire in the fourteenth century. It reached its greatest heights under the gentle and scholarly Ulugh Bey, a grandson of Tamerlane born in 1394. Under the Timurids, Persia enjoyed a renaissance of the arts and sciences, and Ulugh Bey gave special attention to astronomy. He is said to have understood the *Almagest* in its entirety, and to have been extremely competent in mathematics. He built a large observatory at Samarcand, equipped it with numerous large instruments, and made it one of the wonders of the Eastern world in medieval times. By means of a gnomon some 180 feet high he and his assistants determined the latitude of Samarcand and the obliquity of the ecliptic with considerable precision, and with other large instruments fixed the value of precession as 1° in seventy years. They also collected material for the *Zig* (1437), a series of improved astronomical tables which became widely renowned in Europe until as late as the seventeenth century. Incorporated with the *Zig* was a catalogue of stars which constituted the most perfect collection which had appeared up to that time. All Ptolemy's stars, with the exception of twenty-seven which were too far south to be visible from Samarcand, were examined and given places in celestial latitude and longitude not just to degrees, but even to minutes of arc.

Ulugh Bey was a great student of astrology, and when he calculated his sons' nativities he found that the heavens favoured the prospects of his younger son. The elder, being slighted, denounced the predictions as spurious and rebelled against his father. Civil war ensued, and in a battle near Samarcand, Ulugh Bey was defeated and compelled to seek safety in flight. Abdallatif, the elder son, thereupon seized the reins of power, and in 1449 caused the execution of both his father and younger brother—a fact which all Ulugh Bey's astrological art had failed to predict. With his death all serious work in astronomy ceased in the Near East.

To some scholars the Muslims and those they employed were torchbearers only, the preservers and transmitters of the flame of ancient knowledge which might otherwise have been extinguished before it reached the western world. The main area of transmission, however, was Moslem Spain on the doorstep of Latin Western Europe and the opening subject of the next chapter. As far as the scholastic philosophy of the thirteenth century was concerned, and this applies also to its astronomical elements, the treasures of Muslim culture were revealed when the victorious Christians of northern Spain captured Toledo, Seville, and Cordova. Other scholars see the Muslims in a more creative rôle as a people who generally enriched but occasionally debased the scientific heritage of the Hellenes. Their work in alchemy and medicine was great indeed, but although they infused these subjects with new vigour, they strengthened rather than broke the links between them. Arabian medicine, with the additional use of drugs and remedies from the Far East, was unavowedly Greek. The Muslims considered surgery to be inferior to medicine and its practice an activity fit only for barbers and handimen. Religion forbade blood-shedding among Moslems, human dissection was forbidden, and anatomy and physiology became debased versions of Greek teachings. In chemistry, however, they not only absorbed the ancient lore of the East but also made notable advances. As this interest embraced organic substances they became the founders of pharmacology. Nor should we overlook the value of the often herculean labours of their compilers, interpreters, and commentators. Through their activities old knowledge became incorporated into a body of living thought and as such passed without a break into Western Europe.

At the everyday level, astronomy was concerned with the determination of direction and time. The poor nature of Arabian maps and cartography meant that the stars were often the only guides for mariners at sea and the trade caravans travelling at night across the steppes of Asia and Africa. At such times a knowledge of the constellations, all liberally sprinkled with star reference names, was of considerable importance. Again, the religious calendar, an entirely lunar one, focused attention on the moon and its phases and progress through the twenty-eight mansions. Also connected with the Moslem faith, and dependent on the findings of astronomers, was the importance for every believer, wherever he might be in the vast empire, of knowing the direction of the Holy City, Mecca, and the correct hour of prayer.

Direction at sea was assisted by the use of the mariner's compass, knowledge of which the Arabians probably obtained from the Chinese. It appears to have been used during and after the eleventh century, and at first consisted of a shaped lodestone floated on wood in a bowl of water. It was then found that the lodestone could impart its directive property to slender pieces of iron, and these mounted on vertical pivots constituted the first compass needle. Yet, wherever possible, Arabian navigators 'hugged the coastline' and took no chances with unknown currents and sudden winds in the open sea. Perhaps it was in this way that they first explored the Indian Ocean and even the South China Sea to Canton. No doubt the seven voyages of Sinbad the Sailor are romantic versions of actual travels in these mysterious Eastern waters. At a much later date, 1498, it was an Arabian pilot, one Ahmad ibn Majid, who piloted Vasco da Gama across the Indian Ocean after his passage via the Cape.

Most Muslim astronomers were also astrologers, for astrology was appraised as a science. Astronomical tables were generally prepared and checked with an eye to their use in astrological predictions. Ptolemy's *Quadripartitum* was among the first books to be translated into Arabic and it received numerous annotations and commentaries. Other books on the subject were entirely Arabic in character, and writers like al-Kindi, al-Balkhi (known as Albumasar), Thabit ibn Qurra, and many others who associated alchemy with astrology, were responsible for a vast heritage of literature on the occult.

The Muslims never fully appreciated Greek astronomy at its highest. They failed to understand the full geometrical significance of Ptolemy's system, otherwise they would not have made it both incredibly complex and a physical absurdity. Their interest and abilities led them to seek practical applications rather than abstract generalities. Thus arithmetic and algebra took precedence over geometry, and until the time of Nasir ed-Din, trigonometry remained subservient to astronomy. Yet through astronomy they were able to develop the elements of spherical trigonometry—to discover new relationships, compile tables, and become extremely adept in the use of trigonometrical ratios—although not expressing them in their functional form.

At its best levels Muslim astronomy was largely the assimilation and checking of Ptolemy's results, for which purpose instruments made to the Greek pattern were used. Craftsmanship in metal-work reached high levels under the Abbasids, and records show that the Baghdad observatory was furnished with the best and latest armillae, astrolabes, quadrants, and sextants. Through Arabian skill and workmanship a flat planispheric astrolabe, a kind of navigational computer, became a particularly versatile, accurate, and even attractive instrument. Those skilled enough to operate it could, among other things, determine the time by direct observation of the altitudes of the sun and stars. Many treatises were written on its design, use, and construction, the first of which appears to have been one by al-Fazari, the Persian astronomer who translated the Hindu *Siddhanta* (see p. 125).

Fixed instruments, like those at the observatories at Baghdad and Damascus, were modelled on the instruments described by Ptolemy and used by Hipparchus. Among them was the armillary sphere, a series of graduated metal rings which represented the main great circles of the heavens. The rings could be orientated with reference to either the horizon and zenith, or the ecliptic and its poles. In the former case one of the fixed rings represented the meridian, whilst a movable ring furnished with sights enabled the measurement of altitudes and azimuths. In the latter case the fixed meridian ring was still retained, but the pivots on which the movable rings could be rotated represented not the zenith and nadir, but the north and south poles of the ecliptic. With this system the positions of stars and planets could be established in terms of celestial latitude and longitude. Perhaps some of the Arabians, and most likely al-Hazen, orientated their armillae equatorially, but it was not until 1534 that this arrangement was first mentioned in Europe, and then by Gemma Frisius. The first large European spherical equatorial armillae were made and used by Tycho Brahe.

The Arabians also developed the quadrant, an instrument mentioned but apparently never used by Ptolemy. This consisted of a divided metal arc of 90° angular extent provided with plumbline and sights, and generally set up permanently in the meridian for ascertaining the meridian altitudes of celestial objects. In the pursuit of ever greater accuracy, instruments were made very large, although in practice the increase in size often led to little or no increase in precision. For observing the meridian altitude of the sun, for instance, Abul Wefa is said to have employed a metal quadrant of 20 feet radius and a great 56-foot sextant of masonry. The Baghdad observatory, with its massive instruments erected on a raised terrace, and all open to the night sky, must have been an impressive and not unexpected sight in this wondrous city of *The Thousand and One Nights*.

CHAPTER IX

GRATIFYING ILLUSIONS

*These orders all gaze upward, and downward
have such conquering might that toward God all
are drawn and draw.*

St Bernard

IN the West, Muslim culture was greatest in Spain and Sicily, and it was through centres of learning at Cordova, Toledo, Seville, and Syracuse that Latin scholars had their first contacts with the Graeco-Arabic tradition. Between them, the Arabs and Berbers conquered most of Spain during the period 711–18, and Sicily fell with the capture of Syracuse in 878. In the tenth century, and under Spanish Omayyad rule, Cordova on the Guadalquivir rivalled Baghdad and vied with Constantinople as the finest and largest city in Europe. Christian travellers, bold enough to risk their necks among infidels, brought back wondrous tales of its great mosque and associated library, which under the learned Caliph Al-Hakem II is said (but with probable exaggeration) to have contained 400,000 volumes.* In addition, the city possessed beautiful buildings, about seventy different libraries, and numerous public baths and hospitals. Travellers told also of the incredible riches with which the city abounded—of beautiful ceramics, delicate traceries in marble, metal and ivory, and immense carpets and fabrics whose colours and intricate designs baffled and delighted the eye. Had their interest extended as far, they would also have become aware of the existence of a vast body of scientific learning, all of which was completely unknown to contemporaneous Latin scholars.

* Largely destroyed by reactionaries after his death in 976.

144

Bottled up in border countries between the Muslim south (Andalusia) and the Pyrenees were small and fractious Christian kingdoms of Leon, Castile, Aragon, and Navarre. Their subjects lived uneasily beside what they regarded as a great hornets' nest of infidelity, and the bolder among them looked forward to the time when Spanish arms could drive the invaders back into Africa. The Muslims, for their part, had no great contacts with their Eastern counterparts, and showed little interest in the peoples to the north of the Pyrenees whom they regarded as barbarians. As one Muslim historian wrote in the eleventh century, the northern 'barbarians' have big bellies, pale bodies, and long and lank hair. 'They lack keenness of understanding,' he continues, 'and clarity of intelligence, and are overcome by ignorance and foolishness, blindness and stupidity.'

Signs that all was not well in the Muslim south began to appear early in the eleventh century. True, Caliph al-Mansur or Almanzor had taken the offensive against the Christian north, and in 1002, the year of his death, had marched into Castile. But his reign was a troubled one, the next twenty-nine years saw considerable internecine strife, and in 1031 the caliphate was abolished. Numerous petty princelings and political parties then fought for supremacy, and eventually reduced Moslem Spain to a state of civil war. The kings of the north naturally seized this golden opportunity, they added to their territories, and in 1085 Alfonso VI of Leon and Castile even pushed far enough southwards to annexe Toledo. About the same time the Normans drove the Berbers out of Sicily, and in 1118, Alfonso I of Aragon captured Saragossa and made it his capital. The slow but gradual decline of Berber–Arabic domination in Spain had begun. Cordova fell in 1236, Seville in 1248, but Granada remained a Moslem centre until as late as 1492.

The leading Arabian astronomer before the Spanish recapture of Toledo was al-Zarkali, known later as Arzachel, who died about 1087. He acquired considerable reputation as an instrument-maker, and during the course of his work in this capacity invented

a new form of astrolabe. He wrote a treatise about it, and both instrument and book (in the Latin translation) proved popular during the Middle Ages. Under his direction a group of astronomers
worked at fresh planetary and trigonometrical tables which were
finally published in 1080 and which became known as the *Toletan
Tables*. One of his suggestions was that the planets move in
ellipses round the earth, but the idea was so contrary to Ptolemaic theory that his contemporaries promptly ignored it. Another
able astrolabist was the French ecclesiastic Gerbert, bishop of
Rheims, then of Ravenna and later Pope Sylvester II from 999 to
1003. So great and unusual was his skill in the making and use of
astrolabes, elaborate water-clocks, and other mechanical devices
that he was popularly regarded as having sold his soul to the
Devil. After receiving a monastic education he lived for some
years near Barcelona in the hope of meeting learned men, but
despite his proximity to Arabian centres of learning he gleaned
little from them. He fairly scoured southern Europe for rare
manuscripts, and in his own words 'spent great sums of money on
scribes and books'.

In the Muslim south about this time the Spanish Moor, Jabir
ben Aflah, operated a small private observatory—probably the
first observatory of its type in Europe. It was located at Seville,
where Jabir studied astrology and observed the heavens with
equatorial armillae similar to those used in the East. He is known
primarily for his treatise on Ptolemaic astronomy which contained
original work on spherical trigonometry and which was subsequently translated by Gherardo of Cremona.

The Christian entry into Toledo at once unlocked the flood-
gates of Arabic learning. Latin scholars from France, Italy, Germany, and Britain lost no time in consulting the intellectual treasures which were now theirs for the asking. The fact that they
knew little or no Arabic, and that in most cases they had to make
translations from translations in no way cooled their ardour. More
important to them was the discovery of a new and exciting body
of living thought, a new world of ideas in theology, law, medicine,

mathematics, astrology, and science as then understood. To assist them were those Muslims who had preferred to remain at Toledo, together with large numbers of learned Jews driven from the south by the religious intolerance of the Berber Almohades. Thus among the translators at Toledo we find the Spanish Christian, Domingo Gundisalvi; converted Jews like Ibn Daud (John Hispalensis) and Pedro Alphonsi; the Englishmen Robert of Chester, Adelard of Bath, and Daniel Morley; Plato of Tivoli and Gherardo of Cremona.

On the advice of Peter the Venerable, abbot of Cluny, Robert of Chester left studies in astrology to translate the Koran (1143) and al-Khwarizmi's algebra (1145). After his return to London in 1149, he drew up a treatise on the astrolabe and calculated a set of astronomical tables, doubtless with a view to their use in astrological prediction. John of Spain translated al-Farghani's textbook on astronomy and several works on astrology; Adelard of Bath, a great scholar and traveller, translated al-Khwarizmi's astronomical tables and an Arabic version of Euclid's *Elements*. The latter he obtained from Cordova by mixing with the infidels there in the disguise of a Mohammedan student. He also wrote about the nature of vision and the astrolabe, dedicating his tract on the the latter to the young Henry Plantagenet. Daniel of Morley left law studies at Paris to acquire the learning of the Arabians. He returned to England 'with an abundant supply of precious volumes'.

About 1150 Eugenius of Palermo translated Ptolemy's *Optics*, and in 1175 Gherardo of Cremona (or Gerard) translated the *Almagest* and the optics of al-Hazen. Unbeknown to Gerard, however, a medical scholar from Salerno had already translated the *Almagest* in 1163, and from a Greek version which had arrived in Sicily from Constantinople. Gerard is said to have scorned the delights of the flesh so that he could the better devote his life to the work of translation. Daniel of Morley saw and heard him at work in Toledo, and was profoundly impressed by his rendering of the *Almagest* into Latin. Altogether, Gerard made about seventy translations from scientific treatises, including Avicenna's great *Canon* of medicine, al-Khwarizmi's algebra, and works by Aristotle, Euclid, Archimedes, Thabit ben Qurra, al-Farbi, and al-Hazen.

At Palermo, another centre of intellectual activity, Emperor Frederick II of the House of Hohenstaufen employed learned Jews to translate Arabic texts. Attached to his court was Michael the Scot, who left his home in Fifeshire to study at Oxford and Paris, and then proceeded to Sicily to act as tutor to the young Emperor. Upon the latter's marriage, Michael spent some years at Toledo learning Arabic, but in 1220 he returned to the service of Frederick who was then Holy Roman Emperor. In his official capacity Michael was court physician and astrologer, activities in which he acquired a great reputation. Legend has it that he introduced miraculous cures, enclosed the Devil in a bottle, and had success in raising the dead (necromancy) and other black arts. Among the many strange tales about him is one which relates the unusual circumstances of his death. Finding through his art that he would die by a stone falling on his head he decided always to wear a steel skull-cap. This he one day doffed during prayers, and with his defences down was killed when a bell-rope dislodged a large stone from the roof. He was an excellent linguist, and under Frederick's patronage organized the reduction of an Arabic version of the *Almagest* (1230) and works by Aristotle and Avicenna.

Emperor Frederick became notorious for his disregard of papal authority, and in 1239 his accumulated political and religious misdemeanours, together with the employment of many infidel Jews, led to his excommunication. Heretic or not, he was sincere but unsuccessful in his attempts to form a united Italy. He founded the university of Naples (1224) in opposition to the papal Bologna, reorganized the medical curriculum at Salerno (1221), regulated medical practice, and gave immense encouragement to art, literature, and science. Michael is supposed to have predicted that Frederick would meet his death at iron gates in a town named after Flora. The Emperor therefore shunned Florence, for its leading church possessed iron gates, but he nevertheless died in

1250 in a room attached to the remains of an iron gateway and at a town called Fiorentino.

Whilst at Pisa in 1225, Frederick met Leonardo Fibonacci, the celebrated algebraist. He was the author of the *Liber Abaci* (1202), through which Arabic numerals came into more general use, at first among the merchants of Italy. A mathematical tournament was held, in which Fibonacci was the only visiting mathematician who could provide full solutions to all the problems set. Fibonacci's algebra, like that of the Arabians, was rhetorical; well over three centuries had to elapse before algebraists became fully aware of the merits and immense possibilities of an easily manipulated symbolism.

By the end of the thirteenth century, Arabic versions of the works of numerous classical authors were being used in the cathedral schools and universities of the Latin West. Unfortunately for science, however, much of this material was of doubtful value, and for this the translators and copyists were partly to blame. Imperfections and obscurities arose owing to the very difficulties of translation and interpretation. Arabic technical terms often received loose Latin equivalents, and several translators were human enough to exaggerate any teaching that savoured of the marvellous. It therefore transpired that many Latin texts were but travesties of their Greek originals—that the early scholars who studied these texts deluded themselves when they believed they were reconstructing the philosophy of Aristotle and others. Still more deplorable was the passive and uncritical attitude of these scholars. They absorbed and stored their knowledge, looking backwards instead of forwards, and accepting their intellectual heritage without criticism or without attempting to put it to the acid test of experience. Instead of exploring the new and original levels indicated to them, they were generally content to examine the old foundations in minute detail.

These and other factors had important effects on astronomy. Through the uncritical outlook of the schoolmen, Ptolemy was not studied as directly as was then possible, but rather through commentaries and popular expositions. Free translations of Alfraganus and Albategnius were widely read in the schools, and in 1217, Michael Scot introduced the astronomy of another equally attractive author. This was al-Bitrugi or Alpetragius, a Muslim of Cordova, who about 1190 had rejected Ptolemy's epicycles and introduced a wholly inadequate adaptation of Aristotle's world-system of homocentric spheres. It was, of course, the full physical picture of the cosmos painted by the Arabians which appealed so strongly to the medieval mind—Ptolemy's geometrical artifices were, by themselves, considered far too threadbare.

Hence when the Englishman John of Holywood, or Johannes de Sacrobosco, as he was more generally called, decided to produce a university text-book on astronomy, he relied largely on Alfraganus and Albategnius for his material, even to the point of copying their mistakes without question. Little is known for certain about him, and it is a moot question whether his native town was Holywood or Halifax, or whether he was from England at all. He did, however, spend the greater part of his life at Paris, teaching astrology and mathematics at the university there until his death in 1256. Basically Aristotelian, and although innocent of epicycles and eccentric circles, Sacrobosco's *Sphaera Mundi* became a set text-book in university curricula. With its altogether too naïve conception of the celestial motions it was frequently re-edited, commented upon, and translated into French, German, Spanish, and Italian. Such was its universal popularity that after the invention of printing and until 1647 it went through at least sixty-five Latin editions.

Before the early years of the thirteenth century, schools and universities knew Aristotle merely as the author of works on logic —nothing was known of his great contributions to astronomy, physics, and natural history, But after the fall of Constantinople in 1204, Greek versions of Aristotle's scientific writings entered Italy and underwent speedy but poor translation into Latin. From Toledo came translations of Arabic versions of Aristotle's texts, and in 1217 Michael the Scot translated an extensive commentary made by the free-thinking Cordovan philosopher Ibn Rushd, or Averroes. Small wonder, therefore, that the Church viewed the arrival of this pagan flood with concern and then with alarm. In 1209, and at a Provincial Council held in Paris, a somewhat ineffectual ban was imposed on all Aristotle's scientific writings.

Yet material so attractive and far-reaching could not be brushed aside in this way. Albertus Magnus, a Dominican of Cologne, spent his best years first paraphrasing the whole of Aristotle's science and philosophy and then synthesizing it with Christian theology. In his discussion of cosmology he considerably modified the writings of Averroes, adopted a simplified but scientifically useless version of the system of Alpetragius, and presented Aristotle as an ally of Christianity. His scheme of the world embodied items which we would now consider to be unnecessary trimmings —the stars and planets in the guise of God's instruments, heavenly spheres of the purest aether, magical stones, celestial virtues, and astrological influences— and rejected the all-important concepts introduced by Hipparchus and Ptolemy. His pupil, Thomas Aquinas, author of the orthodox Catholic faith and a kind of spiritual Euclid, made Aristotle the sole arbiter of scientific thought. He at least realized that Aristotle's system of concentric crystalline spheres was a compromise—that it was suitable for showing only the grosser phenomena of astronomy, but necessary for supporting the faith and authority of the Church. In brief, and thanks to the efforts of these two great Dominican scholars, Aristotle's cosmology became an integral part of the Catholic faith, and Aristotle himself an authority second only in infallibility to Holy Writ and the Fathers of the Church.

By the thirteenth century the cosmos had become clothed with moral purpose right down to its smallest part. At the centre stood the earth, a mere speck compared with the vastness of the whole and yet a globe of immense size in relation to objects upon its surface. Deep within its bowels were the infernal regions, ruled over by Lucifer, a fallen prince of angels imprisoned up to his chest in ice. His great wings occupied the very centre of the earth, and thus of the universe. Hence man, animals, and plants found themselves living betwixt heaven and hell in a realm of change and corruption which extended through the two layers of air and fire to the sphere of the moon. Yet these temporal disadvantages, coupled with his physical insignificance, in no way clouded judgement as to Man's spiritual importance. The possession of an immortal soul, on the contrary, enabled him to share the nature of the angelic spirits and, perchance, eventually to join the Elect in Paradise. He was at once the apple of God's eye and the centre and object of Creation.

Just as Jerusalem was regarded as the centre of inhabited lands, so the Triune God dwelt directly above the Holy City, but far distant in the tenth Empyrean heaven. Like Aristotle's *Primum Mobile* or Prime Mover, He was Himself unmoved, and was appropriately seated on a throne of light. In awful majesty He ordered all things below, presided over the heavens, and contemplated the beauty of His creation. Like Ra of olden times He did not play solitaire but was accompanied by the adoring and hymning souls of the faithful. 'The souls, which are called immortal,' Plato had written, 'when they come to the summit of Heaven, go outside and stand on the roof, and as they stand, they are carried round by its revolution and behold the things that are outside the Heaven.' However far distant the stars, God was farther, an arrangement which went well until the sixteenth century, when Thomas Digges and the heretical Giordano Bruno suggested that the stars are arranged in depth to an infinite distance.

Also present in the heavens was a hierarchy of the heavenly host, who, like the minions of Zeus, acted as messengers and interceded on behalf of erring mankind. These divinities also operated as propelling agents, the Seraphim being responsible for moving the sphere of the *Primum Mobile*, the Cherubim for moving the sphere of stars—and so on through orders of Thrones, Dominations, Virtues, Powers, Principalities, and Archangels, down to the ministering Angels of the crystalline sphere of the moon. Below the moon, and analogous to the celestial arrays were orders of ecclesiastics, demons, plants, animals, and elements —even to orders of excellence among the organs of the body. If the medieval universe was large and complex it was nevertheless well organized, essentially rational, and permeated with purpose.

This was the general picture, for writers and artists differed in points of detail. Some favoured eleven spheres; that is, the usual set with the addition of two outside the azure sphere of the fixed stars. One of these looked after the precessional motion, the other controlled trepidation, and above all was limitless space and the Olympian throne of the Almighty. Some aimed at greater simplicity and placed Mercury, Venus, Mars, and Jupiter in one thick sphere; the heavenly hierarchy of angels were then arranged in the space between this sphere and that of Saturn. Others so simplified the system that it lost its astronomical significance altogether, but doubtless elevated the thoughts of its pious and uncritical beholders.

An interesting variation of the medieval scheme is seen in the immortal *Divine Comedy* of Dante Alighieri. Dante was born in Florence about 1265 and therefore lived in the period we are discussing. He tells how in a vision he travelled with the shade of Virgil into the subterranean cavity of Hell, to which he gives a funnel shape with its apex at the earth's centre. The travellers penetrate through the various chambers of torment where they find astrologers (Michael the Scot among them), hypocrites, thieves, heretics, blasphemers, and other reprobates, and reach the frozen lake and Lucifer himself. Beside the fiend they climb down and yet up, for they are at the earth's centre, but once clear of his dreaded presence they continue unhindered towards Purgatory. This last place is in the antipodes to Jerusalem and rises in terraces from the sea like an immense staged pyramid. Like a Babylonian ziggurat it has seven stages and is surmounted by Eden, or the earthly Paradise; here they find those souls, which, although repentant, have to make up their arrears of temporal punishment before they can enter Heaven.

For Dante, all the spheres of heaven constitute the heavenly Paradise, and the poet rises through each one, for they are solid yet purely transparent to light and spiritual essences. Eventually he reaches the all-embracing tenth Empyrean, where St Bernard invites him to lift his eyes to 'The Love which moves the sun and the other stars', and where the vision ends.

Dante was deeply learned in the astronomy of his time, and his works are full of interesting references to this, his favourite science. Yet his thoughts are continually coloured by astrological doctrine, for in his time astronomy was generally identified with astrology—at least with those aspects of astrology which dealt with the various virtues and effects of stars and planets. Judicial astrology, it must be remembered, was found acceptable by the Church and by intellectuals at universities who taught 'the seven liberal arts'—namely, the trivium (grammar, dialectic, and rhetoric) and the quadrivium (geometry, arithmetic, astronomy, and music). Only in a few cases were astrologers arraigned by the Church, and then usually because they were rash enough to disregard repeated warnings. Such appears to have been the case with Peter of Abano, a professor at the university of Padua, who dared to suggest that miracles could be naturally explained. His natural death in 1315 saved him from the stake, but his body was exhumed and burnt. Less fortunate was Cecco d'Ascoli, or Cichus, a professor of astrology at Bologna, who was burned at the stake at Florence in 1327, six years after Dante's death. Perhaps his studies led him too deep into sorcery and necromancy, perhaps his sharp tongue had jibed at Church doctrines. Perhaps the charge that his poem *l'Acerba* was an invidious parody of Dante's *Divine Comedy* was trumped-up on the part of strong political enemies. At any rate, the Church was then by no means hostile to judicial astrology, and its Inquisition, set up to safeguard the Faith, had comparatively few serious brushes with its devotees.

While astrology continued to have a large following, and while there would always be those ready to exploit its anti-theological aspects, the Church had no option, but to be ever vigilant. As early as the seventh century, and before Spain came under Arabic domination, St Isidore of Seville had distinguished between what he called 'natural' and 'superstitious' astrology. The former embraced medical and meteorological astrology and divination from comets. The latter he branded as 'the science practised by the mathematicii who read prophesies in the heavens and place the twelve [zodiacal] constellations as rulers over the members of man's body and soul, and predict the nativities and dispositions of men by the courses of the stars'. Some five hundred years later, John of Salisbury, for four years bishop of Chartres, made a similar distinction. His main complaint was that astrologers magnified the influence of the stars at the expense of God's control of nature and human free-will. Astrology, he felt, encroached upon the domain of Divine Majesty, since it pretended to foretell events which only God alone controlled. Yet the issue was clear enough. So long as it set no limit to the power of God—so long as cometary and planetary influences were regarded as no more than parts of the Divine Plan—the Church had little fault to find with astrology. Subservience and submission to Church doctrines in this, as in all other subjects, were demanded but not always achieved.

The medical aspects of astrology had a large following during the Middle Ages, and the comments of Pliny and the fourth-century authors Firmicus Maternus and Avienus in these connections were eagerly studied. 'A doctor without astrology', it was said, 'is like an eye that cannot see.' Physicians, like Chaucer's learned 'Doctour of Phisik', were 'grounded in astronomye', kept an astrological eye on the wheeling heavens, and learnt how to interpret astronomical tables and cast nativities. Even Roger Bacon, perhaps the most enlightened of medieval scholars, considered that 'a physician who knows not how to take into account the positions and aspects of the planets can effect nothing in the healing art except by chance and good fortune'.

The usual bedside procedure was to ascertain the precise time when the patient fell sick and then to draw up his horoscope. His condition and its future course were then ascertained according to (*a*) whether the malady contained hot and dry or cold and wet principles, (*b*) the influential planets in his life, and (*c*) the aspects of those planets with reference to the fateful 'houses' or 'mansions' of heaven, that is, with respect to particular groups of zodiacal constellations. They also claimed to be able to assess what force each planet was exerting on appropriate parts of the human body. Unstable Mercury, for instance, presided over the liver, generative Venus ruled the genitals, and valiant Mars governed the kidneys. Each zodiacal sign, moreover, presided over a region of the body such as the head, neck, shoulders, thorax, and abdomen. Particularly important was the prediction of the time of a crisis, or when an illness took a sudden turn towards health or death. 'The times of crises are changed', says Peter Apian, '. . . by causes, strength, symptoms, stars, medicine and care.'

Foremost in potency was the moon, for its moist and watery nature was supposed to affect both the quantity of blood in the human body and, in accordance with Galen's teaching, its rhythmic ebb and flow. Hence before he bled his patient the learned leach noted the age, location, and aspect of the moon. We are told, for instance, that as King Harold's father, Godwin, lay speechless on his death-bed, his physicians decided not to bleed him because of the growing phase of the moon. Likewise Hildegard of Bingen, the eleventh-century abbess and mystic famed for her cures and visions, believed that the blood is augmented as the moon approaches its full and then diminishes as it wanes. 'And since the moon has this changeability the phases in itself,' she writes, 'therefore the moisture in man has its vicissitudes and mutability in pain, in labour, in wisdom, and in prosperity.' In Hildegard's time, blood-letting was regularly practised in monasteries both for health reasons and to assist the inmates in withstanding the lusts of the flesh.

At the close of the twelfth century, Alexander Neckam, the foster-brother of Richard I, who ended his life as abbot of Cirencester, recorded how moonbeams, shining through a hole in the wall of a stable, became concentrated in one spot of the back of a horse and thereby caused the death of a groom standing nearby! Neckam's contemporary, Michael Scot, wrote an extensive *Introduction to Astrology* in which he not only listed the parts of the body affected by the signs of the zodiac, but discussed the moon's influence on health, menstruation, tree-felling, and pig-slaughtering. Similar ideas, probably gleaned from Pliny, were given by the august Spanish physician, Arnold of Villanova, who cured his protector Pope Boniface VIII of the stone. Arnold considered the age of the moon with respect to the regulation of health, and suggested that physicians should allow for the lunar influence when they prescribe salves, lotions, ointments, eye-washes, and poultices. In 1307 his contemporary at Montpellier, Bernard de Gordon, wrote that venesection must not be practised when the moon is in the constellation of the Twins (*Gemini*), since an injured vein cannot then repair itself and death will follow. He once prepared to bleed himself, but thought better of it when he found that the moon was in *Gemini*. Curiosity got the better of astrology, however, and he proceeded with the operation. He lived to write his treatise *Phlebotomy* and to admit that this particular bleeding did him more good than any previous one.

The ancient idea of the lunar influence on the humours of the brain was prominent throughout the medieval period. Absence of the moon, says Hildegard, whether at new moon or during eclipse, is liable to produce epilepsy in a person whose brain already contains dry humours. Even as late as 1627 we find Francis Bacon, Lord Chancellor of England under James I, repeating Pliny's belief that oysters and cockles undergo a monthly swelling, and accepting the old idea that the brains of animals are fullest when the moon is full.

Astrological doctrines plagued medicine just as long as men were willing to wear the mental blinkers of scholasticism. By ransacking ancient authors, close reasoning and hair-splitting logic, the schoolmen convinced themselves and their contemporaries

157

that the volumes of brains and cockles, say, vary with the phases of the moon. Now this view, so unreasonable to the modern mind, becomes less so when three such diverse objects are removed from their modern categories and regrouped under the common heading of growth. This, in effect, is what the medieval schoolmen did, for their picture of the universe recognized little distinction between the workings of the brain, cockles, and the moon. The heavens or macrocosm, conceived of as God's living garment, clothed and influenced the earth down to its smallest part, and found itself reflected in Man, the microcosm. Just as the heavens contained seven spheres and the book of *Revelation* told of seven angels, seven plagues, seven golden vials, and a seven-headed Beast, so the head of Man had seven apertures, a coincidence which led Petrus Hispanus, later Pope John XXI and the only pope whom Dante met in Paradise, to argue that the eye has seven tunics or coats. In such a mental climate William Anglicus could claim in 1219 to predict by astrology the colour and substance of human urine without seeing it, John of Arderne (1377) extolled its curative effects as an eye lotion, and alchemists deluded themselves by thinking that chemical operations performed under a waxing moon produced the purest metals. Years of patient observation and experiment, of the direct and close study of nature, had to elapse before these fancies were dispelled, but, as will be seen in the next chapter, a start was made in the very period we are discussing.

Since perfectly natural events were assigned to supernatural causes, it is not surprising that unusual phenomena like shooting stars, comets, planetary conjunctions and oppositions, and aurorae continued to be regarded as harbingers of disaster. The tenth century in Europe was not a particularly happy one—indeed, the dark side with its wars, plagues, pestilences, and poverty was never far distant in medieval life. In the year 1000, for example, the idea that the general resurrection predicted in *Revelation* was imminent gained widespread acceptance. For a thousand years 'the dragon, that old serpent, which is the Devil, and Satan' had been bound in

Hell, but in that year he would break loose and 'deceive the nations'. Hence when a comet appeared in that very year it plunged Europe into the deepest despair. As it rode the heavens a brilliant meteor appeared. 'The heavens opened,' writes an eye-witness, 'and a kind of flaming torch fell upon the earth, leaving behind a long track of light like the path of a flash of lightning. Its brightness was so great that it frightened not only those who were in the fields, but even those who were in their houses. As this opening in the sky slowly closed, men saw with horror the figure of a dragon, whose feet were blue, and whose head seemed to grow larger and larger.'

The belief that comets portended the fall of kings is expressed by the historian William of Malmesbury. Speaking of the death of Henry I, King of France, by poison, he tells of the comet of 1060 which apparently denoted a change in kingdoms. As the comet sent out its long and 'fiery train' across the sky, William either saw or heard that Elmer, a monk of Malmesbury abbey, had bowed down in terror. 'Thou art come!' cried the monk. 'A matter of lamentation to many a mother art thou come; I have seen thee long since; but I now behold thee much more terrible, threatening to hurl destruction on this country.' Destruction did follow, but not until six years later, when a return of Halley's comet seemed to augur the success of Norman arms and the defeat and death of Harold. The dreaded visitant appeared in April 1066, and for seven nights seemed to hover over England like a great demon star. Few Saxons were bold enough to declare outright that it presaged the death of Harold in particular, but after the decisive affray at Battle this verdict was unanimous. The strength of the claim lessened somewhat when news reached England that the same comet had also preceded the death of the Emperor Constantius Ducas at Constantinople.

Matilda of Flanders, the wife of William the Conqueror, later worked all the most memorable episodes of the 1066 invasion on a large tapestry known as the Bayeux tapestry. In one of the scenes a troubled Harold is being told of the preparations of

William, whilst overhead is Halley's comet with the legend: *Isti Mirant Stella.**

Church records, town and monastery chronicles, and early Chinese annals often provide brief and not altogether reliable items of cometary information. Other sources are manuscript tracts and texts which are largely speculative in that they deal with the physical nature and astrological significance of comets. Latin scholars drew their material from Arabic sources—especially the *Centiloquium*, an astrological text attributed to Ptolemy, and Aristotle's *Meteorologica*, which tells of the physics of shooting stars and comets. An early contributor to the subject was the Franciscan scholastic, Robert Grosseteste, who lived from about 1175 to 1253. This teacher, statesman, Chancellor of Oxford University, and Bishop of Lincoln for the last eighteen years of his life, took the entire range of knowledge as his province. In astronomy he wrote about the spheres, optics, calendar reform, and comets. He had little good to say about astrology, but his tract *De Cometis* shows that he still believed in the old idea of astral influences. Comets, he writes, are caused by a celestial virtue which irradiates certain parts of the earth. Spiritual exhalations are released, and these rise to be ignited in the fiery heights of the sublunar sphere. This heavenly acquisition, however, leaves the earth with a comparative but temporary excess of corruption, and objects upon it are therefore more prone to the ravages of death and disease.

Grosseteste's disciple, the erudite Franciscan friar Roger Bacon, showed particular interest in the comet of 1264. It appeared late in July of that year and became one of the finest objects yet recorded—its tail is said to have been over 90° long. The Italian monk Ristoro d'Arezzo said that it rose at three o'clock in the morning, had great rays like a mane, and appeared as large as a mountain. It continued visible for over two months, growing fainter and fainter towards the end of September as it travelled towards the south and disappeared on October 3. Bacon was im-

* A loose form of the correct Latin *Isti Mirantur Stellam.*

pressed by the rapidity with which the 'great and dreadful' apparition approached the planet Mars, then in the sign of the Bull. This, he considered, was a clear indication that Mars had caused the comet to be generated; it also foreboded dreadful slaughter among Christians in southern Europe. In France, Aegidius of Lessines, a monk of the Dominican order, hearing that many minds seemed stupefied by the appearance of the comet of 1264, wrote a small treatise of enlightenment. In Tuscany, the comet was said to herald the war in which Manfred and Conrad were slain, and also the death of Pope Urban IV, for he died on October 2 of the same year.

Bacon was not alone in his belief that Mars could influence and perhaps generate a comet. Albertus Magnus regarded that planet as the 'prime mover' where comets are concerned, although he conceded that a conjunction of Jupiter and Mars might stir up 'scintillations and coruscations and running fires'. The rule of Mars, he says, 'signifies wars and death of inhabitants and disturbances of rulers'. Hence a comet spreads destruction upon the earth and decimates the ranks of potentates by reason of their fame and 'since their periods have more planetary dignity'. Peter of Limoges, the learned canon of Evreux, wrote on the structure of the eye and observed the comets of early 1299 and late 1301 with a Ptolemaic instrument known as the torquetum. On the former date Mercury, Venus, and Jupiter were all visible, and Mars seemed to attract the tail as the comet moved northwards. Peter therefore considered that the apparition had its generation from Mercury, and that although it was influenced by Mars, its baneful effects were mitigated by the opposing actions of Venus and Jupiter. Mars was also favourably disposed when Geoffrey of Meaux observed the bright comet of 1315 from Paris, which he found had risen in the Virgin where Jupiter was.

These brief comments give some idea of the general attitude of the learned towards comets. Their physical aspects also received attention, but mainly with the intention of finding a physical basis for astrological doctrine. For the same reason courses were plotted, tail directions noted, and planetary aspects considered—futile labour, for the final conclusions invariably as distressing as they had always been. Comets seldom portended anything other than disaster.

In order to attract attention to the deaths of important personages, early chroniclers sometimes recorded comets that were never seen. On other occasions the visitant even expedited the death of the great—they became ill, and on seeing the comet, became so convinced that their days were numbered that they died soon afterwards. This appears to have been the case when Gian Galeazzo Visconti, the tyrant of Pavia, was helped from his sick-bed to see the first of the two comets of 1402 from his casement window. When he saw the comet he remarked: 'I render thanks to God for having decreed that my death should be announced to me by this celestial sign.' To the great joy of his many enemies, he died soon afterwards.

Early records have sometimes proven useful when astronomers have wished to identify the past appearances of periodic comets. The difficulty here, however, is that long-period comets come under the long-term gravitational influences of the planets, especially massive Jupiter, and fail to return to the vicinity of the sun at constant intervals. The classic example is the comet known as 'Halley's comet'. By noting the resemblance between the paths and appearances of the comets of 1531, 1607, and 1682, Edmund Halley felt pretty sure that a single object of period seventy-five or seventy-six years was involved. This led him to predict a probable return in 1758, but his death in 1742 prevented him seeing the actual return seventeen years later. Halley also surmised that the visitant of 1456 was a member of this series, for it had been described as having an altogether brilliant appearance. Chinese annalists recorded that its tail was 60° long, and shaped something like that of a peacock; its head was at one time round, and appeared about as large as 'a bull's eye'. Some, like Purbach and Paolo dal Toscanelli, regarded it as an opportunity for making better measurements, others satisfied popular demands by publishing tracts about its nature and significance, and the majority spoke of either victory or defeat. Europe was then troubled by the military successes of Sultan Mahomet II, and both Christians and infidels thought that the Deity would favour their own particular aims. Pope Calixtus III is said to have stated that the comet had the form of a cross; Mahomet announced that it had the form of a *yataghan* (a long Turkish dagger) and was a blessing of the Prophet's. Nevertheless the victory went to the Christians, for in the same year John Hunyadi drove the Turks back from the walls of Belgrade.

Sometimes the records fail to distinguish between a comet, the rayed arcs of aurorae, or an impressive meteor. The following account by the historian Nicetas is of this ambiguous nature, for although he calls the marvellous apparition of 1182 a comet, it was more likely an exceptionally bright meteor or a vivid auroral display. 'After the Romans were driven from Constantinople,' Nicetas writes, 'a prognostic was seen of the excesses and crimes to which Andronicus the Emperor of Constantinople was to abandon himself. A comet appeared in the heavens similar to a writhing serpent; sometimes it extended itself, sometimes it drew itself in; sometimes, to the great terror of the spectators, it opened a huge mouth; it seemed that as if, thirsting for human blood, it was upon the point of satiating itself.' Observations of 'streamers strewn among the stars', 'fiery comets which remain fixed', 'lofty columns of flame', and 'prodigious armies in the skies' evidently refer to striking displays of northern lights. Jacobus Angelus of Ulm saw one of these late in 1399, and records that a bright heavenly fire lit the countryside for long after sunset. In the autumn of the following year he saw what was apparently a large meteor—a flame as long as a lance came across the heavens and disappeared behind the pinnacle of a house. These two phenomena, coupled with violent thunderstorms during the summer of 1401, were thought to herald the bright comet of 1402.

One Church record of unusual interest concerns the fall of a large meteoric stone on November 7, 1492, at Ensisheim on the

Upper Rhine. The fall of the great stone at Aegos Potamoi in 468 B.C. is but one instance of numerous similar events recorded by historians. About 650 B.C. and again in 343 B.C. a shower of stones fell on Rome, while in 616 B.C., and according to Chinese annalists, a single stone crashed down on several chariots and killed ten men. Another meteorite fell in Arabia in the seventh century A.D., and after being built into a corner of the Kaaba at Mecca, received the kisses of generations of devout Moslems. The stone at Ensisheim fell in broad daylight and made a deep hole in a wheatfield. 'There were remarkable conversations about this stone,' the authorities record, 'but the learned said they knew not what it was; for it was beyond the ordinary course of nature that such a large stone should smite the Earth, from the height of the air, but that it was really a miracle of God; for, before that time, never anything was heard like it, nor seen, nor described. When they found that stone, it had entered into the Earth to the depth of a man's stature, which everybody explained to be the will of God that it should be found; and the noise of it was heard at Lucerne, at Vitting, and in many other places, so loud, that it was believed that houses had been overturned: and as the King Maximilian was here the Monday after St Catherine's Day of the same year, his Royal Excellency ordered the stone which had fallen to be brought to the castle; and after having conversed a long time about it with the noblemen, he said that the people of Ensisheim should take it, and order it to be hung up in the church, and not allow anybody to take anything from it. His Excellency, however, took two pieces of it, of which he kept one, and sent the other to Duke Sigismund of Austria; and they spoke a great deal about this stone, which they suspended in the choir, where it still is; and a great many people came to see it.' When found the stone weighed 260 lb; its remains, as far as is known, are still preserved in the little church at Ensisheim.

Early observers apparently failed to see any connection between these stony masses and shooting stars, then generally regarded as being purely atmospheric in origin. In accordance with

the physics of Aristotle, meteors were believed to be lofty emana-
tions from the earth which, unlike comets, were extinguished
soon after being kindled. Not all scholars were of this opinion,
however, and a few subscribed to the teachings of Anaxagoras by
suggesting that meteors have a cosmical origin. The first-century
writer and philosopher Plutarch, for instance, had anticipated
modern views with the comment that meteors 'are heavenly
bodies which fall or are cast down in consequence of an inter-
mission or irregularity of the force of rotation and are precipitated
not only on inhabited countries, but also in greater numbers beyond these into the great sea so that they remain concealed'. We
know now that they are rocks and metallic masses drawn from
outer space by the earth's attraction and ignited by friction with
the earth's atmosphere. The vast majority are dissipated long before they reach the ground, but those that do are clearly of the
larger variety. Siderites (all-iron meteorites) are rare; the rest are
referred to as aerolites (stones) and siderolites (stone and iron).

Although shooting stars may be seen on any clear night, they
are more abundant at certain times of the year, especially in
August and November. Sometimes showers of meteors would
flash across the night sky like thousands of luminous devils or the
bright tears of a saint. In November, A.D. 472, the sky at Constantinople appeared to be on fire with flying meteors, while another shower in the same month caused the Arabians to call the
year 902 the 'Year of Stars'. Eastern chroniclers record that in
October 1202, shooting stars 'appeared like waves upon the sky,
towards the east and west; they flew about like grasshoppers, and
were dispersed from left to right; this lasted till daybreak: the
people were alarmed'. During another remarkable display seen
from England and France on April 4, 1095, the stars fell 'like a
shower of rain from heaven upon the Earth' and an eye-witness,
having noticed where a meteorite fell, 'cast water upon it, which
was raised in steam with a great noise and boiling'. From these
and other dated accounts it is evident that the meteor streams
which give rise to the *Lyrids*, *Perseids*, and *Leonids* (see page 235)

continued to do so over many centuries, but with apparently greater abundance in the past than in recent times.

The widespread belief that the world would end in the year 1000 was associated with the old idea of the Great or Platonic Year. Berosus, Plato, Seneca, and others had all entertained the notion that after 36,000 years events would repeat themselves. Like the Babylonians of old, they knew that two or more planets sometimes appear in the same part of the zodiac—that they are in conjunction as we say in astronomy. Specially significant from an astrological viewpoint was the unique occasion when all the planets, together with the sun and moon, appeared in conjunction. Nothing less than a cosmic catastrophe could then take place, the nature of the event being determined by the particular zodiacal constellation favoured by this seven-fold assemblage. If it happened in *Pisces*, *Capricornus*, or *Aquarius* a universal deluge would engulf mankind; if in *Leo* or *Cancer*, cosmic fire would shrivel the earth; if elsewhere in the zodiac, storms, fires, and earthquakes would bring disaster no less complete.

For the year 1000 astrologers predicted great tempests, earthquakes, and mortality among men, 'but', says Rigord, a writer of that period, 'the event very soon belied their predictions'. To many people the occasion of a total solar eclipse was often mistaken as a sign of the Last Judgement. In parts of England in 1140, for example, darkness came over the land and caught men unawares whilst they sat at their midday meals. Some lit candles and others rushed out fearing, as William of Malmesbury puts it, 'the ancient chaos was about to return'. In 1198 another alarm of the end of the world was raised, but for a quite different reason—it was reported that Antichrist was born in Babylon!

Conjunctions of three or four planets were also considered to presage disaster. The great bubonic plague, called the Black Death, began to travel westwards from the Crimea in 1346, and was supposed to be caused through either the malice of the Jews or the 1345 conjunction in Aquarius of Mars, Jupiter, and Saturn. This terrible visitation, whose effects are graphically described by

Boccaccio in his *Decameron* (1353), eventually carried off a quarter of Europe's population and had an immense demoralizing effect. Late in the following century the notorious Pope Alexander VI and his reprobate son Cesare Borgia, both masters of monstrous orgies, contracted a contagious disease which their physician ascribed to a four-fold conjunction of the planets in Scorpio. In 1530, the versatile Girolamo Fracastoro, physician, astronomer, geologist, and fellow-student with Copernicus, wrote a medical poem in which he christened it 'Syphilis or the Gallic Disease'. Sixteen years later he was able to stress its contagious nature, showing at the same time that its causation was anything but celestial. Yet another physician, the unenlightened Petrus Maynardus, had no hesitation in predicting that the disease would end with the four-fold conjunction in 1584.

CHAPTER X

PRACTICAL DIGRESSIONS

Science is acquired at great expense, by frequent vigils, by great expenditure of time, by sedulous diligence of labour, by vehement application of mind.

Alexander Neckam

MANY questions which have little to no relevance today once engaged the earnest attention of intellectuals. The busy pens of ecclesiastics in early Christendom covered pages in attempts to resolve such difficult questions as: Can Hell become over-crowded? What was the nature and astrological significance of the Star of Bethlehem?* How many angels cans sit on the point of a needle? Were the Magi astrologers? and What is the precise date of the Nativity?

The last question involves our present system of reckoning the years forwards and backwards from the time of the birth of Christ. The former part of this custom is said to have been introduced about 525 by Dionysius Exiguus, a monk of Scythia, who became an abbot of Rome towards the end of the fifth century. The worthy abbot availed himself of a cycle of 532 years which had already been discovered by Victorius Aquitanus, and after which Easter returns at the same date in the Julian calendar. He made the beginning of the first and last of these cycles to coincide with the year on which Octavius assumed the title of Caesar Augustus, and adopted as the first day of the epoch not January

---

* According to Jewish legend a star heralded the births of Abraham and Moses. Heavenly lights were also supposed to have announced the births of Krishna, Buddha, Lao-tse, Aesculapius, Caesar Augustus, and other illustrious leaders.

1, but March 25, the Roman date of the vernal equinox. By doing this he unwittingly made the date of Christ's birth 4 B.C. by our reckoning.

During the Middle Ages, no less than in dynastic Egypt, the regulation of the calendar and the maintenance of a time service were an ecclesiastical function. The Church continued to use the Julian calendar until 1582 (when Pope Gregory XIII issued his bull which established the reformed calendar), and by making the civil and ecclesiastical years both equal to 365¼ days, hoped to ensure that Christians everywhere would keep the numerous religious fasts, feasts, and other observances on the proper days. In practice, however, the all-important festival of Easter gradually arrived earlier and earlier in the year, for the Julian year of 365¼ days is some 11 minutes 14 seconds too long. Now in 325, when the vernal equinox fell on March 21, the General Council of Nicaea had fixed the day of Christ's resurrection as the Sunday after the full moon falling on or next following the vernal equinox. If the full moon fell upon a Sunday, Easter-day would be the next Sunday after. Date and event were therefore regarded as being 'fixed' in the calendar (howbeit with a possible range of 35 days from March 22 to April 25), to retain which the Church adopted the old luni-solar cycle of Meton. On the Julian basis, however, the vernal equinox continued to arrive earlier and earlier at the rate of about one day every 120 years. Disputes over the correct date of Easter naturally arose, but successive General Councils and individual astronomers failed to find a satisfactory remedy.

The Christian day began at sunset and had its temporal hours reckoned from sunset to sunrise. Midday was therefore the sixth hour, so that Christ's death at the ninth hour took place at 3 P.M. by our reckoning. At this hour 'nones' were said in churches, an office later moved backwards to the sixth hour and the origin of our association of 'noon' with midday. Before mechanical clocks came into use, that is, before the fourteenth century, the well-ordered day in abbey and monastery was regulated with reference to a water-clock which more often than not actuated a bell and perhaps even moved a hand round a dial. King Alfred is said to have measured time by noting the drop in heights of burning candles, having first protected the flames with translucent horn covers. Whilst the monasteries had their water-clocks, large notched candles and graduated oil vessels, townsfolk probably relied upon simple rushlights for both light and time. Perhaps it was the unreliability of these graduated lights that led one early chronicler to base his time-scale on the natural functions of man rather on man's devices.

In the absence of a water-clock, monasteries appointed junior brothers to note the changing dispositions of the stars relative to the monastery buildings. The task involved a general knowledge of astronomy—of constellation patterns and star names—and considerable patience. The instructions, as the following example shows, were clear enough.

'On Christmas Day, when you see the Twins lying, as it were, on the dormitory, and Orion over the chapel of All Saints, prepare to ring the bell. And on January 1st, when the bright star [*Arcturus*] in the knee of Artophilax [*Boötes*] is level with the space between the first and second window of the dormitory and lying as it were on the summit of the roof, then go and light the lamps.'

When public mechanical clocks appeared they required frequent attention. They were generally of immense size, the great forged-iron frames containing a ponderous array of pivots, spindles, and gears which operated jacks for the regular striking of bells. Because of imperfections in their construction they were frequently deranged, and until crown wheel, verge escapement, and foliot balance replaced the controlling fan-fly, they needed frequent re-winding. Another early practice was to re-set the clock every morning, for daytime was reckoned from sunrise to sunset and varied with the lengths of the seasons. But as cathedral and turret clocks became more numerous and reliable they dictated rather than depended on the time of sunrise and sunset. Temporal hours gave place to equinoctial hours, operative throughout the year and reckoned from midnight and midday as is done today. Clock-keeping remained responsible work even without these daily adjustments; it involved long hours of attendance, a fair knowledge of mechanics, and no small physical agility.

Records indicate that St Paul's had a public striking clock before 1286, Westminster installed one in 1288, and with an outlay of £30 Canterbury Cathedral followed suit in 1292. About the year 1365, Edward III caused a stone clock-tower to be erected in Palace Yard, Westminster, the mechanism of which struck a bell known as 'Great Tom' and so gave the hour of day to the Courts of Law. This was correctly called a clock (from the French 'cloche'—a 'bell') and its bell, together with others rung only at deaths and coronations, was said to have 'soured all the drink in the town'. Canterbury Cathedral had a new clock-house in 1316, when mechanism was installed to strike five bells including 'Bell Thomas', a great bell of over three tons weight.

In 1344 a dial was added to the mechanism of the St Paul's clock and others soon followed suit, although they each had to make do with one hand—the hour hand. This moved clockwise and therefore in keeping with the direction in which the shadow of a vertical gnomon moves on a horizontal dial. Had clocks been invented in the southern hemisphere, this hand would doubtless have been made to move anti-clockwise. If the mechanism could turn a hand over a dial, it was not unduly difficult to devise supplementary gear-trains for moving devices for showing astronomical phenomena. One of the first astronomical clocks was installed in Norwich Cathedral about 1325. Sets of painted and moving images personified the hours of day and night and the days of the month, whilst gilded and painted plates represented the sun and moon. About the same time Richard of Wallingford, the learned son of a blacksmith and later abbot of St Albans, laboured for many years on an astronomical clock for his monastery. This showed, among other things, the courses of the sun and moon, the rising and setting of the stars, and the ebb and flow of the tides. Another old astronomical clock was believed to have been

made about 1335 by Peter Lightfoot, a monk of Glastonbury
Abbey. The clock was also supposed to have been moved to its
present position in Wells Cathedral at the time of the dissolution
of the monasteries, but records show that a clock was in use there
in 1392. Visitors to Wells can see the great 6½-foot dial of an
astronomical clock, complete with moon phases and minute divisions, but the great face conceals a comparatively recent mechanism. The original movement, with subsequent alterations, is preserved in the Science Museum, London. Another old and yet
largely original timepiece in this museum is the 1348 turret
clock formerly used at Dover Castle. Both exhibits with their
weighted driving barrels, massive gear-trains, verge escapements,
and regulating 'foliot' balances are of exceptional interest. The
largest, and at the same time the most famous astronomical clock,
is the one in Strasbourg Cathedral. It dates back to 1571, being
modelled on a much earlier mechanism installed in 1370 and of
which only the mechanical cockerel remains.

Another method of time determination was to use a flat or
planispheric astrolabe designed for use at the particular latitude of
observation. As we have already seen, knowledge of this versatile
instrument travelled northwards via Spain, but few astronomers
possessed the necessary ability to make or use it with good effect.
A number of Latin manuscripts, all based on Arabic sources, dealt
with its design and construction, among them one written in 1391
by Geoffrey Chaucer, the celebrated author of *Canterbury Tales*.
Chaucer tells how the astrolabe can be used 'To knowe every
tyme of the day by liht of the sonne, and every tyme of the nyht
by the sterres fixe', but the text is disappointingly short. He wrote
it for 'little Lewis my son', which perhaps explains why the instrument is treated more as a scientific toy than as an instrument of
precision.

According to Dr D. J. Price, Chaucer was probably the author
of the *Equatorie of the Planetis*, a unique folio manuscript written
in Middle English and preserved in the Library of Peterhouse,
Cambridge. Dr Price has made a critical study of this work, which

describes a special mechanical calculator based on the geometry of the Ptolemaic system and used for finding the positions of the planets. Like the astrolabe, it received its greatest development at the hands of the Arabians, and Dr Price has been able to trace it both backwards to eleventh-century Granada and forwards to the Copernican-type *equatorium* made by a seventeenth-century instrument-maker. Only two *equatoria* have as yet been found, one of them engraved on the back of a mid-fourteenth-century astrolabe preserved at Merton College, Oxford.

In Chaucer's time the astrolabe and small quadrant were about the only astronomical instruments in active service. With the traditions of Hipparchus and Ptolemy either forgotten or ignored, and with astrology satisfied with the loose accuracy of the Toletan and Alfonsine Tables, there was no need for large measuring instruments or established observatories. Instead of direct observation of the heavens, scholars dimmed their eyes and minds over the texts of Aristotle. Except for the sporadic activities of individual astrolabists like Robert Grosseteste, Roger of Hereford, Roger Bacon, Richard of Wallingford, Geoffrey Chaucer, and the traveller Nicholas of Lynn, serious work in observational astronomy was almost dead.

The peak of astronomical activity in thirteenth-century Europe occurred at Toledo, the capital of Alfonso X, surnamed 'the Wise', and King of Castile and Leon. Although nominally a Christian, Alfonso encouraged learned Muslims and Jews as translators, interpreters, and instructors in the sciences. He founded a school or academy, placed the learned infidel Abu al-Riquiti in charge, and personally supervised encylopaedic projects in poetry, literature, law, and astronomy. He also compiled a treatise on the virtues of precious stones, and gave the first European description of the game of chess. In astronomy he engaged a Jewish physician, Judah ben Moses Cohen, and numerous assistants to correct any errors in Arabic versions of Ptolemy's *Almagest*. The work involved great expense and labour, but after four years Alfonso had the pleasure of writing the preface to the finished *Alfonsine*

Tables. Computed for the epoch May 30, 1252, the day of Alfonso's accession, the tables contained only a few improvements and embodied no fresh observational material. They were more a compilation of previous results than an original investigation, and as such contained the usual information—lists of positions of the planets, times of eclipses, features of the ecclesiastical calendar, and items of astrological import. Even so, they formed the backbone of much subsequent work and were frequently consulted and quoted until at least the sixteenth century.

The moral attitude towards nature also found expression in medieval cartography. Apart from charts and guides for travellers, especially itineraries for pilgrims and relic-hunters bound for the shrines of the Holy Land, picture maps of a symbolic nature were produced in large numbers. The finest example is preserved in Hereford Cathedral, and was prepared about 1280 by one Richard of Haldinham. This large and circular world-map (known as a psalter-map) fittingly shows Jerusalem at the centre and the terrestrial Paradise at the top. The latter takes the form of a circle, in the centre of which is represented the tree of the knowledge of good and evil, together with Adam and Eve and the crafty serpent. Outside Eden the couple are shown in hasty flight before a driving angel, whilst in the nearby eastern countries occasional pigmies, dragons, satyrs, fauns, and men with mouth and eyes in their chests add to the general interest. Palestine is enlarged to make room for the portrayal of sites hallowed in the Scriptures, and a large tower of Babel sits above the Euphrates. Britain, near the lower edge of the map, is purposely distorted to fit in the circle, and like most of the other countries, bears no resemblance to its actual shape. Smaller circular maps, especially earlier ones, were generally debased versions of the Hereford type. Some were no more than rudimentary diagrams of the Near East with the seas forming a letter T—hence they are generally referred to as T-O maps. As one authority suggests, they were probably used for the edification of the pious and not as aids to travellers. The fact that they are round and flat does not mean that their originators believed the earth also had this shape. On the contrary, the idea of an immense globe and the inseparable idea of circumnavigation were widely current throughout the Middle Ages.

Through Arabian sources, the records of travellers like the friars John, Odoric, and William of Rubruquis, and the diary of the resolute Venetian Marco Polo, cartographers learnt something of the distant lands beyond India. This knowledge, unfortunately, had a distinct bias towards the marvellous. India was a land of magic and wonders, of gems and herbs with remarkable virtues, and of mountains of gold guarded by monsters. In the thirteenth century, William of Auvergne, bishop of Paris, regarded India as the playground of demons driven thence by the spread of Christianity. It was a country for getting quick results with magical images and gems—one can almost detect William's regret that it is so far away. Friar Odoric gives an interesting account of his visit to the Court of the Great Khan at Karakorum, and mentions that he saw astrolabes there. He writes: 'On the one side of the Emperoure's table sitteth many phylosophers of many sciences, some of Astronomie . . . and some have before them Astrolabes of gold, or of precious stones full of sande or of cole brenning [burning], some have horologue [time-keeper] with dight and richly, and many other instruments after their sciences.'

Between 1325 and 1355 Sir John Mandeville was supposed to have travelled to China and back, but his book of travels contains more fiction than fact. He enjoyed a wide popularity, however, especially after the introduction of printing, and Christopher Columbus was one among many who pored over his stories. Mandeville's text makes it abundantly evident that he and his contemporaries believed in a spherical earth and therefore in its eventual circumnavigation. 'Paradise terrestre', he writes, 'is towards the East at the beginning of the earth, but that is not our East that we call where the Son ryseth in those countreys towards Paradise, and then it is midnight in our countrey for the roundnesse of the earth, for the Lord made the earth all rounde in the middest of the fyrmament.' And later: 'In these yles of the land of

Prester John [somewhere beyond India] they are under the earth to us, and other yles there are, whoso wold pursue them for to environ the earth, whoso had grace of God to hold the waye, he mighte come right to the same countreys that he were come of and come from, and so go about the earth.'

Another class of maps, or rather sea-charts (later known as *portolans*), witnesses to the use of the compass in medieval times. Although these vellum charts with their black coastlines marked with ports, bays, rocks, and shoals, depended on no latitude–longitude system, this was no great loss to mariners who sailed in enclosed waters. More important to them were groups of radiating lines, forerunners of the compass rose, which were intended to represent compass bearings from selected places. The magnetic compass, it must be mentioned, was first described in Europe by Peter de Mericourt, generally referred to as Peter the Pilgrim. His treatise concerning it appeared in 1269, but, as we have already suggested, the compass had a much earlier history with the Arabians and Chinese. In Peter's time compass needles and windroses were in use, and navigators had learnt to steer a course relative to one of the bearing lines on a portolan map. They then estimated their progress along the selected line with lead and line, that is, by the principles of dead reckoning. Sea currents and winds might deflect a ship from its course, mist, fog, or darkness might blanket the coastline, but there was always the apparently unfailing reliability of the north-pointing compass needle. This was believed always to point in the direction of the Pole Star, being constrained to do so by some mysterious stellar emanation or virtue. The effects of masses of iron on board or of certain rocks were ignored, and the phenomenon known as the variation was quite unknown. Not until maritime activity moved outside the Mediterranean to the waters of western Africa did latitude observations become really important as a supplement to dead-reckoning navigation.

In the thirteenth century, and when the majority of their learned contemporaries were thinking in terms of miraculous stones, demoniacal powers, and the magical transfer of disease, a small group of Englishmen began to interpret nature in the sober light of their own experience. Knowledge, they believed, could be acquired from the authority vested in theology, together with the exercise of reason in canon law, philosophy *and experimental investigation*. One of the first to stress the value of direct observation and experiment* was the former Oxford scholar Robert Grosseteste, already mentioned in these pages in connection with his views on comets. He also wrote on optics and perspective, no doubt after having studied a Latin translation of al-Hazen. He discussed vision and the effects produced by concave mirrors, and then described the magnifying effects of glass segments. 'This branch of Perspective thoroughly known', he claims, 'shows us how to make large things very far off seem very close at hand, and how to make large objects which are near seem tiny, and how to make distant objects appear as large as we choose, so that it is possible for us to read the smallest letters at an incredible distance, or to count sand or grain or grass or any other minute objects.'

Grosseteste also wrote about the break-up of 'visual rays' when they encounter new media, of the angular subtenses of objects, and of the need for further experiments to investigate these things. He was quite sure that magnifying effects are not due to any occult force in the glass but rather to the shape of its surfaces, or, as he puts it, 'great things seem small and conversely according to the shape given the interposed transparent object'.

Grosseteste's younger contemporaries, the austere and tireless John Peckham, later Archbishop of Canterbury, and the versatile Roger Bacon, also interested themselves in these effects, and, like their scholastic master, considered that optical images are not due to magical influences but rather to natural causes. In his *Perspectiva Communis*, published at Milan in 1482, Peckham discussed propositions of optics, the construction of the eye and the nature of vision, and the effects of variously shaped mirrors and lenses.

---

* Not to be interpreted in the modern sense, for Grosseteste had no conception of physical laws.

Bacon followed in the same vein, and mentioned how a plano-convex lens could be made useful 'to old persons and to those with weak eyes'. 'If the letters of a book or any minute objects', he writes, 'be viewed through a lesser segment of a sphere of glass or crystal, whose plane base is laid upon them, they will appear far better and larger.'

Even at this comparatively late period lenses were still rare and expensive items and when Grosseteste and Bacon refer to their magnifying effects, they write about something which was then quite new and extraordinary. Their comments on the apparent magnification of distant objects, however, must not be interpreted as being due to some particular *combination* of lenses, as in a tele-scope, but rather as the effect which can be seen when a weak convex lens is held at some appreciable distance from the eye. Neither Grosseteste at Lincoln nor Bacon at Oxford can be credited with the invention of the refracting telescope.

Bacon, like Plato nearly two thousand years earlier, believed in the power of mathematics 'to unfold the causes of all things and to give a sufficient explanation of human and Divine phenomena'. It was no 'Black Art', as many of his deluded contemporaries per-sisted in believing. Proof of this, he says, can be seen in the writ-ings of the learned Grosseteste and Adam Marsh, another Oxford Franciscan. Mathematics, he considered, is of such a nature that it can be mastered only by diligent application over thirty to forty years—which perhaps accounts for his own lack of contributions to the subject. Although sufficiently a traditionalist to believe that 'perfect knowledge' can be obtained only by a diligent study of Holy Writ, he knew that mathematics was the key that would un-lock the door of the sciences of his day. But his own interests covered too wide a field for him to canalize his efforts in mathe-matics. He prepared a Greek grammar, grappled with the prob-lems of the calendar, drew up astronomical tables, dabbled in alchemy, and wrote on theology, geography, and the knowledge of the times. He was also the first European to write about gun-powder (an earlier Chinese invention), and, with characteristic intuitive genius, predicted propelled vehicles and heavier-than-air flight.

Another thirteenth-century 'experimenter' was Witelo or Vitellio of Poland, who appears to have made most of his optical observations at Padua and Viterbo in Italy. He wrote a treatise on optics, drawing his material largely from a Latin translation of al-Hazen. He adopted and extended the Arabian's geometrical treatment, avoided the sensational, and was well aware of the need for further experiments: 'Experience more than books', he writes, 'will teach the varied possibilities of [optical] images.' Experiments need to be supported by sound theoretical considerations, however, and these were not forthcoming in optics until several centuries later. Unlike Grosseteste, Vitellio agreed with al-Hazen in regarding light as composed of numerous rays; the rays emanate from objects perceived, and possess virtues which can be strengthened or weakened through reflection and refraction. Even Vitellio found it difficult to escape from the astrological doctrine of 'virtues'.

Bacon at no time explicitly suggested that the magnifying effects of lenses could be utilized for forming spectacles—that is, paired lenses temporarily positioned before the eyes. Yet, unbeknown to him, and apparently only a few years before his death in 1294, spectacles had already appeared both in China and in Italy. The year and even the century of their appearance in China is not known with certainty, but both clear and coloured convex lenses of crystal appear to have been used as curative agents in ocular disease as early as the time of Confucius, that is, in the sixth century B.C. During his travels in China at the close of the thirteenth century, Marco Polo noticed that old people used convex lenses to read print, information which he is supposed to have recorded when he dictated his memoirs during 1295 to 1299. His reference may well have given rise to the so-called invention of spectacles in the West, an invention usually ascribed to Alexandro della Spina, a Dominican monk of Pisa, and to his friend, Salvino d'Armati of Florence. Little is known about either 'inventor' save that Spina died in 1313 and that Armati's tomb-stone was said to bear the inscription: 'Here lies Salvino degli Armati, inventor of spectacles; May God pardon his sins.'

The first Italian spectacle-makers were fortunate in having access to well-established glassworks at Venice, an industry handed down to the Venetians by the Byzantine traders. As the demand and manufacture of spectacles for reading purposes increased, so news of their miraculous effects passed to other countries. Sight was restored to the aged, not by bathing the eyes in holy water or by using one of John of Arderne's urinary lotions, but by lodging on the nose horn or leather folding frames containing convex lenses of glass or crystal. Demand quickly outstripped production, and all manner of folk began to enter this lucrative field of lens- and frame-making. To protect their common interests, therefore (and at the same time to monopolize the market), craftsmen in the work followed the example of those in other crafts and formed their own 'gilds' and 'mysterys'. By the early sixteenth century, and with the availability of printed books and concave lenses for correcting short-sightedness, there were flourishing spectacle-making 'gilds' at centres in Italy, Germany, France, and Holland. As a direct result of this movement the refracting telescope was invented, howbeit quite by chance.

CHAPTER XI

BREAKS WITH TRADITION

Just as we ought to give credit not to the tool, the use of which erected the structure, but to the workman who used it, so the stars and their motions have effects, but we should ascribe these not to the stars themselves, but to God who rules them and who is the ruler of all causes and origins.

Peter Apian

ABOUT the year 1438 a young man called Georg Purbach arrived at the university of Vienna from his native town of Beurbach, near Linz. From his great interest in astronomy and unusual abilities in mathematics, it soon became apparent that Purbach was no ordinary scholar. He completed his studies in the seven liberal arts with outstanding success, and was recommended to the patronage of the distinguished Rhinelander, Nicholas of Cusa or Cardinal Cusanus. The cardinal had himself followed with success an exacting career in scholarship. His real name was Nicholas Krebs, and he was the son of a boat-owner and fisherman of Cues in the Moselle valley. The elder Krebs had neither time nor respect for learning, and he is said to have once knocked his studious son overboard with an oar. The boy eventually ran away from home and was fortunate in coming under the protection of Count Theodoric of Manderscheid. He was sent to a school where Thomas à Kempis and Erasmus were educated, entered the university of Heidelberg, and in 1417 proceeded to Padua, where he studied canon law and mathematics. His rapid rise to worldly fame followed his appointment at Cologne as secretary to Canon Orsini, an Italian intellectual and the Apostolic Legate in Germany. Not only did Cusa's subsequent travels in Europe provide opportunities for meeting leading thinkers, but his work in monastic and cathedral libraries facilitated the study and collection of numerous rare texts.

A great lover of astronomy and mathematics, Cusa made ineffectual attempts to reform the calendar and square the circle. He possessed remarkable skill in logic, entertained Neo-Platonic ideas, and knew something of the value of experimental procedures. From his particular view of nature he not only anticipated the idea that all motion is relative, but also considered that a rotating and lateral moving earth would account for the diurnal motion of the heavens just as well as would a set of rotating spheres. It is not surprising, therefore, that this versatile and boldly speculative ecclesiastic made a profound impression on his younger companion. Purbach returned to Vienna full of noble intentions, and upon his appointment as professor of mathematics, settled down to making this subject and astronomy his life's work.

Purbach had long felt that students of mathematics needed a text more exact than Sacrobosco's *De Spherae*. He therefore planned a new work on planetary motions, published later in 1460, which incorporated epicycles but retained the old hypothesis of material celestial spheres. In addition, he prepared a textbook of arithmetic and a table of eclipses.

In 1451, Purbach found that he was teaching a youthful model of himself in the person of Johannes Müller of Königsberg, better known as Regiomontanus. Regiomontanus was then fifteen years old, fresh from elementary studies at a school in Leipzig, and so apt a student that he readily became Purbach's assistant and then his friend. Master and pupil together studied a Latin version of the *Almagest*, and Purbach decided to write a new and detailed commentary, for which he prepared a table of trigonometrical sines. More important, they constructed their own sighting instruments and made observations from an upper room in the university. They checked their latitude, the obliquity of the ecliptic, and the times of the equinoxes, and still believing in the spurious trepidation or oscillation of precession, attempted to determine its amount. As they observed the places of the stars and, like Hipparchus, marked them on a globe, they noted the effect of precession from Ptolemy's time to the year 1450. They observed the positions of the planets, and by referring to a copy of the *Alfonsine Tables*, then 200 years old, found that both the moon and Mars in particular were well away from their predicted places. In this last respect two possibilities arose: either the tables were wrongly computed from theory, or else current theory itself was at fault—perhaps through the shortcomings of translators.

Whatever may have been their ultimate intentions, the two astronomers were confronted with an unexpected solution to their problem when in 1460 Cardinal Bessarion arrived in Vienna on a mission for the Pope. He told them that he possessed a Greek copy of the *Almagest*, that he knew of the existence of many more original texts, and that it was his earnest wish to make these works more widely known. A Greek by birth, and as Bishop of Nicaea, Bessarion had accompanied the Byzantine Emperor on his journey to the Council of Ferrara in 1438. With him came some 800 Greek manuscripts, and when Bessarion decided to remain in Italy, his texts and enthusiasm for learning did much to stimulate the growing interest in Greek literature. By the time he met Purbach and Regiomontanus he had already started a Latin commentary on the *Almagest*, but not having time to complete it, suggested that Purbach returned with him to Italy for that purpose.

Purbach assented, but on condition that Regiomontanus joined him. Unfortunately for their plans, however, and almost on the eve of departure, Purbach died. Regiomontanus thereupon undertook to see the work through himself, and in the spring of 1461 accompanied Bessarion to Italy. His first task was to master Greek, and for some three years during his patron's absence in Greece he studied this subject at Rome, Ferrara, Padua, and Venice. He was by no means alone in this interest, for when Constantinople, the last direct heir of ancient Greece, fell to the Turks in 1453, many learned Greeks fled to Italy and there sowed the seeds of a great

interest in classical literature. Patrons of art and letters were eager
to share in this Hellenistic legacy—to help rediscover the meaning
and beauty of the culture of the ancient world. Greek grammars,
dictionaries, and manuals were rare and highly prized, for they
were keys which could unlock an intellectual treasure-house more
wondrous than anything Moslem Spain had produced.

Regiomontanus soon became interested in Greek mathematics;
he prepared translations of Apollonius's treatise on conic sections
and the mechanics of Archimedes, and read a copy of the algebra
of Diophantus which had arrived for the Vatican library. In 1464
he wrote the larger part of his own *De Triangulis*, a treatise on
plane and spherical trigonometry which gave numerous problems
and their solution by the use of the sine and cosine. In this year
also Bessarion returned from his travels, and Regiomontanus accompanied him from Venice to Rome. Here he completed the
translation of the *Almagest* from the Greek (printed at Venice in
1496), and collected the last of the many manuscripts which he
intended to take back to Germany and study at his leisure.

Regiomontanus returned to Vienna in 1465, taught there for a
short while as professor of mathematics, and then moved to Buda-
pest on the invitation of Matthias Corvinus, King of Hungary and
Bohemia. Matthias was an enlightened ruler for the times; he
thought highly of astrology, collected books, and was attracted by
anything connected with ancient Greece. He caused his agents to
scour eastern Europe for Greek texts scattered abroad with the fall
of Constantinople, and as a result had assembled a magnificent
library. But if Regiomontanus found the library attractive he had
little opportunity for using it. Shortly after his arrival, king and
country were involved in war. Once again he was on his travels,
but this time he wisely chose the direction of Nürnberg.

Regiomontanus probably felt by this time that he had seen
enough of texts and libraries. He needed peace, money, and instruments so that he might practise astronomy in the Alexandrian way.
Only by actual observations could he test his ideas and form satisfactory conclusions. Nürnberg amply met his needs. The city was

then one of the chief centres of German industry and literary life
and stood in direct commercial relationship with Italy. It was a
prosperous city—a city of prudent merchants, wise professional
men, and industrious artisans. Nowhere in Germany did the
wealthier classes show such willingness to support art and science.
Among the artisans were printers, metal-workers, wood-carvers,
and makers of spectacles, clocks, sundials, and compasses, so that
when our astronomer wished to equip his observatory, he had no
difficulty in finding skilled craftsmen.

The observatory and its instruments were provided by Bernard Walther, a wealthy citizen who, although older in years and
far richer in pocket, was happy to work for Regiomontanus as an
assistant. Regiomontanus designed the necessary instruments, and
Walther saw that only the best craftsmen in Nürnberg were commissioned to make them. Regiomontanus planned the writing of
new works and revised commentaries, and Walther purchased one
of the new mechanical marvels of the age—a printing press. In his
capacity of assistant, Walther made observations for comparison
purposes, shared in the work of plotting the course of the comet
of 1472, and after his master's death maintained the observatory
until his own decease in 1504. He commented on a feature largely
overlooked since al-Hazen mentioned it—the apparent elevation
of the setting sun due to atmospheric refraction—and was the
first astronomer to use weight-driven mechanical clocks for
measuring time in astronomical observations.

Under such favourable circumstances Regiomontanus could
have done invaluable work at Nürnberg. In 1474, however, Pope
Sixtus IV wished to make a new move towards solving the problems of the Julian calendar and requested Regiomontanus's assistance at Rome. The unfortunate astronomer, greatly reluctant at
leaving his work, arrived at Rome towards the end of 1475. On
July 6 of the following year he died, apparently from the plague.
According to one rumour he was poisoned by the sons of George
Trabezonde in revenge for his adverse criticism of their father's
inaccurate translation of the *Almagest*; a not unlikely fate, since

violent death by poison or dagger was then of daily occurrence in Rome.

Regiomontanus had only four years at Nürnberg, and his death at the early age of forty meant that his work stopped when he was at the height of his career. During the last period he published an edition of Purbach's book on planetary theory, a table of sines to every minute and tangents to every degree, several calendars and almanacs for the information of the literate public, and in 1474 a thirty-one-year almanac or *Ephemerides* 'where you may every day see the true motion of all the planets, of the moon's nodes with the aspects of the moon to the sun and planets, the eclipses of the luminaries; and in the fronts of the pages are marked the latitudes'. He also found time to develop a variety of observing instruments based on those described in the *Almagest*, also a cross-staff or Jacob's staff (invented earlier by Rabbi Levi ben Gerson, 1288–1344, of Barjols in Provence) and a rudimentary type of theodolite. His versatility is also said to have found expression in the invention of a mechanical eagle which flapped its wings by way of salute to Emperor Maximilian I when he entered the city.

The sudden death of Regiomontanus also meant that many of his works were left for posthumous publication. Among these was an important tract on comets based on the systematic observation of the comet of 1472. The majority of astronomers continued to regard comets as omens of disaster and to interpret observations of their courses and appearances in terms of astrological theory. Purbach, however, had broken fresh ground. He tried to measure the distance of Halley's comet during its 1456 return, and Regiomontanus did the same for the visitant of 1472. Regiomontanus first saw the latter object on January 13 and observed it regularly with his instruments until the end of February. He recorded its progress through the constellations, noted the length and direction in which its tail pointed, and with a cross-staff measured the angular size of the head and differences in its position relative to the star *Spica*. He concluded that it was at least 8,200 German miles away, or, as we say in astronomy, that its parallax was not greater than 6°—a far too generous limit for an object which was actually several million miles distant. This was the first scientific observation of a comet, and it inspired others in Germany, Walther among them, to follow in this new tradition. Although their instruments were small and far inferior in accuracy to those in far-distant Samarcand, their efforts were none the less praiseworthy.

The immediate popularity of the almanacs and calendars issued by Regiomontanus led other printers to publish similar material, and in 1492 the French *Kalendrier des Bergers* appeared. It aimed at reaching even the lowest classes of the literate population, and through tables and simple diagrams told, among other things, of the changing places of the moon, the dates and significance of eclipses, the progress of the sun in the ecliptic, and how to find movable feasts and Saints' days. The astrological aspects of health and growth, and the problems of time determination with respect to a spherical earth were also outlined. The almanacs of Regiomontanus and the *Kalendrier des Bergers* were thus forerunners of a succession of calendars, almanacs, and prognostications which have appeared without a break down to the present day.* In this way knowledge hitherto associated with deep studies in the 'mathematical arts' was made available to the general public.

Few travellers in the sixteenth century could afford to be without some knowledge of practical astronomy. Watches were expensive rarities (Nürnberg saw the first spring driven clocks in 1500), and only the larger towns possessed public clocks. Yet as long as clouds were absent the sky provided a ready means of telling the time. At night a small astrolabe was used; by day occasional fixed sundials, or better, the traveller's own portable flat-and ring-type sundial answered a similar purpose. By these means he could also determine his direction, and hence, if he possessed a map, some idea of his position. Success depended on the skill (and state) of the observer, as the following story shows. A learned professor of mathematics at Oxford was returning to his lodgings

---

* Almanacs today range from the *Nautical Almanac* used by astronomers to household almanacs containing horoscopes, forecasts, birthday guides, and similar nonsense.

after a deep carousal but somehow lost his way. He thereupon whipped out his astrolabe, but finding the heavens about to fall upon him, dodged sideways and fell into a well-stocked ditch. Passers-by rescued him and put him to bed, from which he arose the next morning resolved to remedy his defects in navigation.

Apart from their great value in astrological predictions, a subject which had intrigued both Purbach and Regiomontanus, the *Ephemerides* of 1474–1504 proved useful in other practical walks of life. Merchants and others who perforce had to face the dangers of night journeys could now plan their movements according to the moon's phase and the hours of moonlight. Ecclesiastics could arrange Church activities for Saints' days and movable feasts well in advance, safe in the knowledge that the new almanac surpassed all others in scope and accuracy. Navigators benefited, for ships from European ports were then penetrating further into uncharted waters where information about time, the moon and tides, and the position of the sun could often decide between success and failure.

The great Portuguese voyages of discovery of the fifteenth and early sixteenth centuries were the direct result of the enthusiasm and energy of Dom Henrique or Prince Henry, the nephew of Edward III of England. Inappropriately called 'Henry the Navigator' by the British, he himself was no great seaman and never sailed with his voyagers. He functioned more as an organizer and planned voyages which had three main objectives: (*a*) to seek a direct route to India via the west coast of Africa, (*b*) to collect gold and so stem the gold shortage which was beginning to imperil the welfare of the peninsula, and (*c*) to bring Christian teaching to the heathen. These goals were to be attained by peaceful means—a striking contrast to the methods of the misguided conquistadors of the sixteenth century. Prince Henry therefore renounced marriage and family ties, and gave his undivided attention to inspiring, planning, and financing voyages of exploration. He studied mathematics and astronomy, trained sailors in the art of navigation, and attracted geographers, cartographers, and instrument-makers to his naval arsenal at Sagres, near Cape St Vincent. By the time of his death in 1460, the same year that Cardinal Bessarion met Regiomontanus at Vienna, the Portuguese had colonized the islands of Porto Santo and Madeira, discovered the Azores, and followed the African coast beyond the great promontory of Cape Verde into the Gulf of Guinea.

In these and subsequent voyages into the Atlantic, latitude determination was of paramount importance. By night the altitude of the Pole Star, obtained with the aid of a quadrant, cross-staff, or astrolabe, indicated (approximately) the latitude of the place of observation. By day the navigator observed the meridian altitude of the sun, and knowing the sun's declination, found his latitude by straightforward subtraction. He obtained the sun's declination (its height above the celestial equator) from appropriate tables such as the *Almanack Perpetuum* of the Jewish mathematician Abraham Zacuto of Salamanca and Saragossa. Simplified versions of these tables, coupled with part of Sacrobosco's *De Sphaera*, and probably bound with a portolan map or maps, were prepared at Sagres and were in use before the *Ephemerides* of Regiomontanus appeared. Difficulty in latitude determination lay not in any technical deficiencies, therefore, but rather in taking the necessary sights—in measuring the vertical angle between the horizon and the sun or the Pole Star. 'It seems to me', wrote one Master John, 'almost impossible to take the height of any star at sea, for I labour much at it and however little the ship rolls, there are mistakes of four or five degrees, so that it can be done only on shore.' On the basis that one degree of the meridian is equivalent to about seventy miles, it will be seen that Master John's concern was not unfounded. He was pilot and astronomer in the 1500 expedition of Pedro Alvares Cabral, which reached Brazil. He was thorough and experienced in his work, and his difficulty, in no way a new one, continued to plague accurate navigation until well into the eighteenth century. In 1731, however, the American glazier Thomas Godfrey introduced a special sea-quadrant, and a year later, and quite independently, John Hadley made a sea-octant. Both instruments were forerunners of the modern nautical sextant.

In 1456, and as the intrepid Alvise da Cadamosto sailed southwards through twenty-five degrees of latitude, he noticed the progressive depression of the altitude of the Pole Star. At the river Gambia this familiar star was so near the northern horizon that it could be seen only in clear weather. To the south Cadamosto saw five bright stars arranged like part of a cross and took them to be the Southern Chariot. The sixth star, α Crucis, was not visible, but it is pretty evident that the five stars were the larger part of the beautiful Southern Cross (*Crux Australis*) of southern skies. Master John, voyaging after the death of Prince Henry, sent his master, King Manöel I, a drawing of this and other constellations; it was also a familiar enough sight to Bartholomew Diaz when he rounded the Cape of Good Hope in 1488. The Southern Cross, however, is some distance from the south celestial pole, which is unmarked by a star of naked-eye brilliance. In consequence, latitudes were calculated from the midday altitudes of the sun, and the appearance of the Southern Cross was generally regarded as an indication that the equator was being reached.

Voyages of exploration as far as Cape Verde meant sailing approximately due south, that is, almost along the meridian of Lisbon. The old problem of longitude did not therefore arise. But when ships reached the Cape and then the Americas, ways of longitude determination were eagerly but unsuccessfully sought. When Columbus sailed westwards in 1492 he travelled in very truth over a lonely and unknown sea; latitude he could determine almost at any time, but he was moving for five weeks essentially in longitude, and in this latter respect was more uncertain of his position than he ever dared tell his crew. Ferdinand Magellan, the first to circumnavigate the globe (1519) and to prove the doctrine of the antipodes, is said to have been 'always busied with pilots, sailing charts and the height of East–West, a subject that has been the perdition of more ignorant Portuguese than the learned have gained by it, for we have so far seen no one who has put it into practice'. The problem of longitude also loomed large when it came to partitioning continental lands and islands discovered, or afterwards to be discovered, by the rival powers of Portugal and Spain. Various papal bulls from 1454 onwards had given the Portuguese a free hand in the west, but later discoveries, especially those of Columbus, involved Spain as well, and some line of territorial demarcation became imperative. By a bull of 1493, and largely at the suggestion of Columbus, Pope Alexander VI established a meridian dividing line at 100 leagues to the west of the Azores. The Portuguese, aware of both the practical difficulty of fixing this line and the fact that it gave nearly all South America to the Spaniards, pressed for a more sensible alternative. They suggested that the division be given by the parallel of latitude through the Canaries, thereby making all South America Portuguese territory. Finally, and by the Treaty of Tordesillas in 1494, everything east of a meridian drawn at a point 370 leagues west of the Cape Verde Islands went to Portugal, whilst Spain had the territories to the west. Portugal thus acquired possession of Brazil, but the practical difficulty of fixing the dividing line led to subsequent infringements of territorial rights. In England and Holland, the papal dispensation of new lands was greeted with derision—neither country had any intention of recognizing an arbitration which they considered to be both presumptuous and intolerable.

The *Ephemerides* of Regiomontanus became known to the mariners of the west through Martin Behaim, a native of Nürnberg, who travelled to Portugal in 1459. He claimed to be one of Regiomontanus's pupils, became interested in voyages of discovery to the west, and with the Jewish astronomer Joseph Vecinho, acted in an advisory capacity to King John II of Portugal. For some time he lived in the Azores, but returned to Nürnberg in 1490, where he was commissioned by the Town Council to construct a large terrestrial globe. This was finished just before Columbus returned from the West Indies and is therefore the last world map to omit the New World. The chief places were laid down on a latitude–longitude grid reference system, but apart from showing the extent of the then-known world, the globe failed to do justice to the extensive geographical knowledge of the Portuguese. In 1493, and probably at the order of Emperor Maximilian I, who was anxious to lay his hands on the riches of India and Cathay via a western route, Behaim returned to Portugal. Here he resumed his acquaintanceship with Columbus and busied himself in planning another enterprise. But nothing came of it, largely because John II and his successor King Manöel were concerned with the more immediate route to the East via the Cape. Continually thwarted in his own projects, Behaim lived to see Vasco da Gama take the first European ship to India by the Cape route. He died in Portugal in 1507.

So far we have sampled a mere fragment of the new spirit of inquiry which was abroad in the fifteenth century. The full scientific renaissance had yet to come, but by 1500 breaks in the medieval intellectual tradition had appeared all over Europe. Italy in particular received and reacted with enthusiasm to the message of rediscovered Greek texts. Following in the spirit of Petrarch and his friend Boccaccio, Italian intellectuals were already in academic revolt against the tyranny and imitative traditions of dogmatic scholasticism. A new and freer approach to knowledge was abroad, an approach which sought wider horizons and which had emancipated reason for its guide and the remains of classical art, literature, and philosophy for its foundation. Led by Florence, cities like Padua, Naples, Milan, and Venice witnessed outbreaks of self-expression in literature, art, and science. Rome also shared in the re-awakening, especially under the prodigal Pope Leo X, for the new individualism had yet fully to undermine the already tottering ecclesiastical structure. Painting, architecture, sculpture, and letters were the first to benefit, and nowhere with such vigour than at Florence. Here during the latter half of the fifteenth century worked such versatile individualists as Alberti, Botticelli, Gherlandaio, Michelangelo, Leonardo da Vinci, and Raphael—

men who put Aristotle to one side, read Plato, Dante, and Pet-rarch, and relied on their own eyes, hands, and intellects.

As art flourished, so did its new basis, geometry. Strong in the belief that a painting should be a faithful reproduction of nature, the Italian masters created the science of linear perspective with its projections, sections, 'vanishing lines', and 'principal vanishing points'. For the first time the three-dimensional world was organized on scientific lines on a two-dimensional canvas. 'Let no one who is not a mathematician read my works,' Leonardo da Vinci once wrote, thereby expressing his conviction along with Plato that nature is amenable to geometrical treatment. Geometry and mathematics therefore received fresh impetus, the more so since artists were also architects and engineers. Leonardo, man of science and the painter of *Mona Lisa* and *The Last Supper*, was a prodigy of versatility. He designed engines of war and a variety of mechanical appliances, studied human and animal anatomy, planned all manner of public buildings, read Vitellio and Peckham on optics, wrote on perspective, and investigated vision and the structure of the eye. The science of painting, he declares, 'is the mother of perspective, that is, of the science of visual rays'. In astronomy he gave the correct explanation of the appearance known familiarly as 'the old moon in the arms of the new moon'. On this occasion the new moon appears as a thin, bright, silver crescent, and the old moon as a greyish remainder due to the earthshine or sunlight reflected from the earth. Hitherto the earth-shine had been attributed to the faint glow of the moon itself or otherwise to illumination of the moon's surface by the planet Venus.

Leonardo died in 1519, by which time Albrecht Dürer had returned from studies in Italy to spread Italian influence north of the Alps. A celebrated painter and sculptor, Dürer prepared spirited wood-engravings of the forty-eight classical constellation figures. When published in 1515 at Nürnberg they appeared on a pair of circular planispheres, one for the northern and one for the southern hemisphere. Dürer's figures were of such excellence that they were copied with but few changes by Bayer (1603), Flamsteed (1729), and others. In 1536, Peter Apian, professor of mathematics at Ingolstadt, produced a similar sky map for the northern hemisphere only, but the constellation figures differed from those of Dürer. Apian is perhaps better known as the author of two sumptuous volumes on astronomy called *Astronomicum Caesarem* or *Caesar's Astronomy* (1540), a copy of which with its interesting cardboard volvelles or movable diagrams was sent to enlarge the ideas of Henry VIII.

Neither Dürer nor Apian gave any special attention to *Crux Australis*, although by this time Amerigo Vespucci and others had brought back much more information about the southern stars. Johann Bayer, who in 1603 produced the first star atlas, showed *Crux Australis* as a cross, but not as a separate constellation. To the existing forty-eight constellations he added twelve new ones for the southern hemisphere, among them the Toucan (*Toucana*), the Peacock (*Pavo*), and the Fly (*Musca Australis*). He also affixed Greek letters to the stars according to their brightnesses, but his orders are often in error owing, no doubt, to his too great a reliance on Ptolemy's estimates. The constellation of the Southern Cross was first portrayed by Augustus Royer, who published a sectional planisphere in 1679.

Coupled with the interest shown in geometry and perspective was the rapid growth of symbolic mathematics at the hands of zealous algebraists like Stifel, Niccolo Fontana (nicknamed Tartaglia), Cardan, Ferrari, and Vieta. At the time their work had little bearing on astronomy, still being faithfully served by trigonometry, but Vieta's systematic application of algebra to both plane and spherical trigonometry promised much for the future. The next and greatest single mathematical contribution to astronomy was undoubtedly the invention of logarithms by John Napier of Merchiston, Scotland, in 1614, and independently six years later by Joost Bürgi, clockmaker to Rudolph II at Prague.

Astrology and Pythagorean number mysticism were favourite

studies with many mathematicians, for one aided and abetted the other. Some of the ablest minds of the sixteenth century spent long hours over Ptolemy's *Quadripartitum* and the mystic study of star-polygons and magic squares. Jerome Cardan, whose name is still associated with the solution of cubic equations, was particularly active in this respect. Convinced that unlucky stars ruled his nativity he seems to have abandoned himself to the vices and excesses of the times, and almost to the point of madness. Fits of debauchery and gambling chequered his career as a student and continued when he practised physic in Italy and Scotland. Yet he was appointed professor of medicine at Padua and Pavia and became no less famous for his mathematical achievements as for his abilities as a physician. In 1560 his elder son went to the scaffold for poisoning his wife, and about the same time Cardan chastised his younger son (who was following in father's footsteps) by cutting off his ears. Alarmed at the public hostility aroused by this outrage, Cardan solicited and obtained the protection of Pope Gregory XIII. He moved hastily to Bologna, but only to outrage public feelings at home and abroad by publishing a horoscope of Christ and an uncomplimentary horoscope of Luther. Rome alone proffered a forgiving hand, and in 1571 he became a pensioner of the Pope in return for services as astrologer to the papal court. This descent to comparative servitude seemed to confirm his horoscope; according to one story he even committed suicide so that his horoscope would remain true to the end.

Another exceptional character of the same period was the Swiss physician and alchemist Theophrastus Bombast von Hohenheim, better known as Paracelsus. During his lifetime, and like Cardan, he was branded as a drunken charlatan and disreputable braggart, yet he too taught medicine at a university. In 1526, and through the influence of Erasmus, Paracelsus became city physician and lecturer in medicine at Basle, where he shocked the public and his superiors by lecturing in German and not in Latin, by soiling his hands over furnaces and alchemical apparatus, and by dispensing with all ancient authority. As he threw the works of

Galen and Avicenna on a bonfire he expressed the hope that their authors were likewise situated. 'My beard knows more than you and your writers,' he stated; 'my shoe-buckles are more learned than Galen or Avicenna.' Nor were contemporaneous authorities spared the lash of his tongue: 'He who depends on the pope rests on sand, he who depends on Zwingli rests on hollow ground, he who depends on Luther depends on a reed. They all deem themselves each above the other, and denounce one another as Antichrists, heathens and heretics, and they are but three pairs of breeches from one cloth.'

By working in the laboratory of the Schwazer mines in the Tyrol, Paracelsus had become expert in metals and their ores. This knowledge he applied to medicine, which, he believed, rested largely on astrology and alchemy—astrology because the stars and planets affect our internal organs, and alchemy because the human body is composed of the *tria prima* or three principles, sulphur, mercury, and salt. His own picture of astrology differed markedly from that painted by his contemporaries. He despised those who believed in horoscopes—who, like Cardan and others, denied human free-will. 'The stars', he writes, 'compel nothing in us, they make and form nothing, they cause no resemblance, and no inclination. They of themselves are perfectly free, and so are we.' Yet with all his iconoclasm he clothed medicine with numerous vital spirits or *archaei* which acted as presiding agencies within the body and had functions similar to the three spirits of the very Galenic medicine he was so anxious to overthrow. Whilst an appropriate spirit had control of the stomach, for example, the process of digestion could nevertheless be influenced by the stars. Hence Saturn could so affect a man's stomach that his nature became morose or Saturnine. It was a physician's responsibility, therefore, to rebalance the stomachial brew by adding the appropriate metals.

Paracelsus was a great traveller, but his opinions gave him no other choice. He stayed at Basle for only two years, leaving behind many enemies and a reputation which temporarily shook established medicine to its foundations. After further wanderings in Switzerland and Bavaria he died at Salzburg in 1541.

As if the times were not exciting or dangerous enough, two mathematical practitioners gave out that the world was about to end. The first, Johann Stöffler, a supposed pupil of Regiomontanus, found that Mars, Jupiter, and Saturn would be in conjunction in the sign of the Fishes on February 20, 1524, and thereupon predicted a universal deluge. He was then professor of mathematics at Tübingen, and had so great a reputation that his prediction terrified all Germany. People living in maritime provinces almost gave their lands away, and many bought or built boats in readiness. A doctor of Toulouse named Auriol even made himself an ark large enough to hold all his family, friends and possessions. When February came not a drop of rain fell, and Western Europe experienced one of its driest months. Stöffler appears to have been as angry as his German dupes at this disappointing turn in events, but such was his vanity that he predicted another end-of-the-world event for 1588—knowing full well that he would not live to see it.

The second prediction, for October 3, 1533, came about when Michael Stifel, a Lutheran pastor and student of mathematics, juggled with the mystic numbers in the books of *Revelation* and *Daniel*. The fact that he had previously calculated that Pope Leo X was the superhuman Beast mentioned in *Revelation* should have warned his hearers. Nevertheless the peasants of Holzdorf accepted his assurances, sold their goods and gave up all idea of work. On the fateful day he arose early, and with a great multitude spent the morning with open-air prayers and hymns. But pastor and flock looked in vain for signs in the heavens and the coming of the Lord. Aware at length of the full extent of Stifel's deception, the angry peasants would have lynched him had he not sought refuge in Wittenberg prison. He was eventually released through the personal intervention of Luther, and no doubt after giving assurances that he would never again indulge in prophecy.

Germans soon forgot Stöffler's scare of 1524, but not the Peasants'War of the following year which caused the death of 100,000 to 150,000 people. Born from oppression and fanned by fanatical preachers, the revolution threw Germany into tumult from the Alps to Westphalia. In terms of history the war was just another episode in that vast European movement known as the Reformation, a movement which saw the birth of Protestantism and the recession of the power of Rome. 'Satan,' writes Luther after the event, 'who formerly raised the Pope, the Emperor, the Prince and the terrible revolt of the peasants against the Gospel, has now changed his methods. It is through sects, heresies, and the spirit of falsehood that he seeks to overcome us.'

Although he believed in good and evil spirits, called comets 'harlot stars', and is said to have once hurled an inkpot at the Devil, Luther waged unceasing war on the religious immaturity of the times. With devastating zeal he attacked the sale of indulgences, the cult of saints, relics, and images, and the host of superstitious fancies and customs which made a mockery of the Gospel teaching. Most of all he hated the 'detestable heresies' of astrology, magic, alchemy, and divination, which he regarded as abominations derived from that 'babylon of *Revelation*', Rome. But it needed more than Luther's invective and system of propaganda to bridle the then growing interest in pseudo-science and mysticism. Ever since 326, when Helena, the mother of Constantine, stated that she had dug up the cross of Christ, relics had poured into the churches of Europe. There were bits of the anatomies of departed saints, samples of the blood of Christ and the milk of the Virgin, and parts of the crown of thorns and of His garments. All were supposed to possess magical powers and were regularly used for curing the sick and exorcizing demons. Popular belief in witches, fairies, love-potions, prowling devils, and magical pills shows that folk in the sixteenth century were no less credulous than the 'mob' in Seneca's time. Nor were these beliefs the sole prerogative of the masses. The period which saw Copernicus re-ordering celestial revolutions found Frederick the Wise arranging his collection of nearly 5,000 holy relics, and the distinguished Elizabethan mathematician John Dee soliciting co-operative demons to raise the dead. Kings and princes supported witch-hunts and rooted out heretics, yet magicians and astrologers flourished on their bounties. In 1517 Nicholas Kratzer was appointed astrologer to Henry VIII at £20 a year. A little later Dee advised the future Queen Elizabeth on astrology, and during his travels abroad worked for a time under the eccentric Emperor Rudolph II at Prague. Tycho Brahe, the greatest astronomer of the sixteenth century, provided horoscopes, astrological reports, and almanacs for the Court of Frederick II of Denmark. Kratzer, Dee, Tycho Brahe, and others in similar positions were no charlatans; on the contrary, they were among the leading mathematicians of their day. Kratzer, the friend of Erasmus and Dürer, made elaborate sundials and taught astronomy at Oxford; Dee, attracted by Copernicanism and a master of Euclid's geometry, wrote on navigation, geography, and perspective; Tycho Brahe founded precisional astronomy. Rather was it the case of astronomy being the handmaiden of astrology—that to most people, kings and princes included, astronomy was palatable only when given strong infusions of astrology. As Kepler neatly put it: 'God provides for every animal his means of sustenance—for astronomers He has provided astrology.'

While Paracelsus brandished the sword of medical reform in Switzerland, Luther in Germany fought for religious reform. In 1520 he consigned a papal bull of excommunication and books on scholastic theology to the flames of a students' bonfire at Wittenberg. He pronounced an anathema on Aristotle because the 'condemned heathen' had attempted to explain everything in terms of natural causes. Since his main attacks, however, were directed against traditional scholastic theology, his conception of the universe was basically Aristotelian. He stood fast to the idea of a fixed and spherical earth (Magellan had proved its sphericity by the voyage of circumnavigation of 1519–22), but otherwise made great changes in the medieval conception of the universe. For him, astral virtues, planetary influences, and directing angels were as nought compared with the all-embracing love of God. 'Is it a stage sky,' he writes, 'such as children imagine, in which Jesus Christ is seated next the Father, with a golden crown on His head? No, the right hand of God is His omnipotence, incomprehensible and incommensurable. . . . God sends not angels or messengers to order and preserve what has gone forth from His hand. He is there Himself, both in the infinitely great and in the infinitely small. It is He who has made the limbs of the body and the smallest fragments thereof, and the marrow of the bones and the leaves of the trees, and He envelops each of His creatures, He penetrates them with His omnipresence as if that creature were Himself. Thus the world is full of God; God fills it but is not confined by it.'

CHAPTER XII

NEW HORIZONS

At last I began to chafe that philosophers could
by no means agree on any one certain theory of
the mechanism of the Universe, wrought for us by
a supremely good and orderly Creator, though in
other respects they investigated with meticulous
care the minutest points relating to its orbits.

Nicholas Copernicus

As long as Italy remained the fountain-head of the new learning, able scholars from far and wide endeavoured to complete their studies at some Italian university. This was the case with Nicholas Kopernik, better known as Copernicus, for after completing a five-year course in the Arts at Cracow, he proceeded to Bologna in 1496 to study canon law. On route to Italy he probably visited Walther at Nürnberg, for he was already keenly interested in astronomy. At the university of Bologna he came under the influence of Domenico Maria da Novara, a keen Neo-Platonist and astronomer. Master and pupil together observed the heavens and no doubt discussed the shortcomings of the Ptolemaic theory as expressed in the *Alfonsine Tables*. After spending some three years at Bologna, Copernicus moved to Rome and then to Padua, where he continued his study of Greek, qualified as a physician, and exchanged ideas with Girolamo Fracastoro, already mentioned in these pages in connection with his poem on syphilis (p. 167).

His studies completed, Copernicus returned to Heilsberg Castle in Polish Prussia, the residence of his uncle and benefactor, Lucas Waczenrode, Bishop of Warmia. Here he began to exchange academic studies for ecclesiastical duties, for in 1497 he had been appointed to a canonry at Frauenburg, the cathedral city of his uncle's diocese.

In 1512 Lucas Waczenrode died, and Copernicus moved into permanent rooms which overlooked the cathedral close. By this time he had so developed new ideas about the nature of the celestial motions that he could not resist communicating them to a few intimate friends. The sun-centred or heliocentric theory thus received its first European expression in the form of a small tract, printed privately and issued to a small number of interested readers. It told of a rotating and mobile earth, of a fixed and central sun, and something of the astronomical consequences of this change in viewpoint. Copernicus's astronomical studies, however, had to be subordinated to manifold administrative duties connected with the cathedral and the Warmian diocese. He was often consulted as a physician, he busied himself with monetary reform even to writing a treatise on currency, and in 1515 he was asked by Pope Leo X to assist in reforming the calendar. This request shows that his reputation as an astronomer was then great, but he declined the task on the grounds that he was still working on the laws of the motions of the sun and moon—that until these were better known he could hold out little hope of success with the calendar. In this respect he showed himself wiser than Regiomontanus, and he was able to continue with his astronomical work without serious interruption. From time to time he observed eclipses, and with a quadrant and 8-foot wooden triquetrum made with his own hands, took occasional measures of the positions of the moon and planets, and probably studied Halley's comet of 1531 and the comet of 1533. Continually in mind was the growing conviction that the idea of a fixed and non-rotating earth was a delusion—that the time-honoured fabric of the Ptolemaic system was both inaccurate and unnecessarily involved. 'Those who have relied on concentrics,' he wrote later, 'though they have often proven that some different motions can be compounded therefrom, have not thereby been able fully to establish a system which agrees with the phenomena. Those again who have devised eccentric systems, though they appear to have well-nigh established the seeming motions by calculations agreeable to their assumptions, have yet made many admissions which seem to violate the first principle of uniformity in motion.'

With Copernicus it was not just a question of suggesting that the earth together with the other planets perambulates about the sun. Nor was it enough to reject the crystal shells of Aristotelian cosmology and rely entirely on circular orbits in space. The heliocentric theory had to be developed up to the point where it agreed with his own and other observations, even if these were all too few and often inaccurate. He was only too well aware of the immense difficulty of unravelling the complexities of the planetary motions. He was also worried as to the philosophical implications of his system, not only because it gave the earth a minor rôle in the cosmos, but also because it was so contrary to the impressions of the senses. The fact that leading Pythagoreans like Philolaus, Hicetus, and Ecphantus had considered the earth's motion about some centre gave him no small comfort. This would have been all the greater had he realized the full measure of Aristarchus's contribution or known something of the ideas of Cardinal Cusanus.

In 1539 Copernicus received a visit from Joachim Retyk or Rheticus, junior professor of mathematics at the Protestant University of Wittenberg. Rheticus had been attracted by talk of Copernicus's great abilities in astronomy, and he doubtless also knew something of the new theory. He arrived at Frauenburg for a short stay, but remained for nearly two years. Under the influence of his enthusiasm, and repeatedly urged by several of his superiors in the Church, Copernicus decided to complete and publish a full account of his ideas. In 1540 Rheticus published at Dantzig a *Narratio Prima* or brief account of the heliocentric system. Two years later he was back in Wittenberg with a copy of the finished manuscript and anxious to proceed with its publication. He soon found that this was not going to be so easy as he had at first imagined; both Luther and Melanchthon spoke disparagingly of the work and threatened to take disciplinary action should it be published in Wittenberg. Luther had already heard of Copernicus and his theory by hearsay, and is said to have been at supper one evening in June 1539, when he spoke of the Polish astronomer as 'the fool who would overturn the whole science of astronomy'. 'Joshua', said he, 'bade the sun stand still at Gibeon and not the earth.' Hence for Luther it is the sun which normally moves and not the earth; to say or think otherwise denied biblical accuracy and constituted heresy. Fortunately an ambitious printer at Nürnberg saw the text in a different light; for him its publication held every promise of being a great financial success.

Rheticus was unable to be personally present to see the manuscript through the press, and it was entrusted to Andrew Osiander, a local and well-known Lutheran clergyman. But when he came face to face with the new doctrines, Osiander became alarmed lest they should be interpreted as being heretical. Copernicus believed in the motion of a physical earth about a physical sun, an idea so contrary to Church teaching that Osiander thought fit to remove the author's preface and replace it by another. Without revealing his own authorship in this connection, he declared in the new preface that the planetary system set forth in the text should be regarded as being hypothetical only and therefore as having no basis in reality. Thus prefaced, and in the winter of 1542–3, the De Revolutionibus Orbium Coelestium came from the presses of Johann Petreius at Nürnberg. Copernicus was then bedridden with paralysis, and did not receive his own copy until May 24, 1543, the day of his death.

Although De Revolutionibus was to have revolutionary effects on astronomy, it nevertheless contained many old ideas. Copernicus at first gives the impression that the sun occupies the very centre of the earth's orbit. 'In the middle of all', he writes, 'sits Sun enthroned. In this most beautiful temple could we place this luminary in any better position from which he can illuminate the whole at once? He is rightly called the Lamp, the Mind, the Ruler of the Universe; Hermes Trismegistus names him the Visible God, Sophocles' Electra calls him the All-seeing. So the Sun sits as upon a royal throne ruling his children the planets which circle round him. The Earth has the Moon at her service. As Aristotle says in his *de Animalibus*, the Moon has the closest relationship with the Earth. Meanwhile the Earth conceives by the Sun, and becomes pregnant with an annual rebirth.' Yet to account for the apparent motion of the sun, and at the same time to retain the Greek idea of uniform velocity in circular orbits, Copernicus had to shift it slightly from the central position, and the 'royal throne' shrank to a point. True to Greek tradition, Copernicus never once doubted that the motion of the heavenly bodies is other than 'uniform, circular, and perpetual, or composed of circular motions'. He therefore found that single circular orbits were alone insufficient, and altogether he had to introduce thirty-four epicycles. He also retained the old idea that the earth is fixed to a revolving radius, and perforce gave an annual conical motion to the earth's axis. The Copernican system, therefore, was Ptolemy reorientated, but in such a way as to offer possibilities of development. As left by its author it needed the influx of new observational material and the ellipses of Kepler to turn it into the so-called Copernican system of today.

Copernicus was evidently pleased to find that a sixth-century author named Martianus Capella had considered the possibility that Mercury and Venus revolve round the sun—an idea which he traced back to early Egyptian times. This arrangement explains why these two planets appear to oscillate to and fro in the sun's vicinity, each alternating in the sky as morning and evening stars. In the Copernican system they both fall within the compass of the earth's orbit, which accounts for their large variations in brightness, and periodical changes in phase. These phases, however, cannot be seen without telescopic aid, and when Galileo first saw the crescent form of Venus in 1610 he knew that the Copernican system was at last vindicated. The 'inferior' position of these planets also means that they sometimes appear to cross or 'transit' the sun's disk, but owing to their small sizes these appearances likewise require telescopic aid. Copernicus was fully aware that these transits can take place, and he cites in likely support an observation made by Averroes who 'saw a kind of black spot when investigating the numerical relation between the Sun and Mercury'. 'This is evidence', he continues, 'that these two bodies are nearer than the Sun.' If Averroes truly saw a spot then it could not have been Mercury, whose diameter is only $\frac{1}{250}$th part of that of the sun, but a large sunspot. The observation is not without interest, for at that time, and until Galileo saw sunspots through his telescope in 1610, most Europeans believed that the sun was too pure a body to be sullied by spots.

By observing the positions of these planets when they were most distant from the sun, Copernicus was able to derive a good idea of the comparative size of their orbits. He applied similar methods to the superior planets, solving in each case the right-angled triangle sun–earth–planet and deriving the comparative distances 1·5, 5·2, and 9 for Mars, Jupiter, and Saturn respectively. From his own observations he also redetermined the distance of the moon, arriving at a value very near to the modern one of 60·27 earth radii or about 240,000 miles. Whereas the average value of the moon's horizontal parallax was found to be about 57 minutes, that of the sun was found to be too small for measurement. Ptolemy accordingly chose the Ptolemaic value of 3 minutes 6 seconds, and since the true value is about 8·8 seconds, made the radius of the earth's orbit some twenty-times too small. His entire system below the orbit of Saturn just exceeded the size of the orbit of Mercury by modern reckoning. He had no means of determining so small an angle as the solar parallax, and, as he once told Rheticus, he looked not for minute accuracy in observation, but rather for a rough agreement between theory and observation. This was a lamentable weakness of the astronomy of his time, but he was sufficiently astute to realize that even if he possessed instruments of the necessary accuracy, his already busy life would have permitted little time in which to employ them to their full advantage.

The *De Revolutionibus*, dedicated to Pope Paul III, made a dignified and comparatively quiet entry into the sixteenth-century world of thought. Only those with an adequate mathematical background could appreciate the full importance of the new ideas, and many astronomers overlooked its physical implications altogether; they regarded it merely as a new way of computing planetary tables. Those with religious scruples no doubt had their prejudices removed by the anonymous preface which they quite naturally assumed Copernicus had written. Out and out enthusiasts like Rheticus and his senior colleague at Wittenberg, Erasmus Reinhold, were at first definitely in the minority.

In 1550 Rheticus published an almanac based on Copernican principles, and a year later Reinhold produced the famous *Prutenic* or *Prussian Tables* through the liberality of Duke Albert of Prussia. Slightly more accurate than the tables of the Toledan school, the *Prutenic Tables* demonstrated the practicability, if not the superiority of the Copernican theory from the viewpoint of making planetary calculations. They did nothing, however, to encourage belief in the physical reality of the heliocentric system. Indeed, observation seemed to negative the idea of a moving earth, for the stars showed no appreciable parallax as the earth swept out its annual circular orbit. Copernicus had foreseen the difficulty and had made the sphere of the stars immeasurably great compared with the size of the earth's orbit. The annual motion of the earth, he says, gives rise to the periodic oscillations of progression and retrogression in the motions of the planets. 'That there are no such phenomena for the fixed stars proves their immeasurable distance, compared to which even the size of the Earth's orbit is negligible and the parallactic effect unnoticeable.' He did not deny the existence of stellar parallax, but considered that it was far too small to be measurable with any of the graduated instruments of his time. This we know to have been a valid argument, but, like the ancient Greeks, many early astronomers disliked the idea of a vast and apparently wasteful space between the orbit of Saturn and the sphere of fixed stars.

Copernicus had little to say about the physical nature of stars and comets—indeed he mentioned the latter only once. Yet it was in these quarters that Aristotelian doctrine received the next blows. From studies of Halley's comet of 1531, the comets of 1532 and 1533, and records of the comet of 1472, Fracastoro at Padua concluded in 1548 that their tails all pointed away from the sun. Two years later, and in the second volume of his *Caesar's Astronomy*, Peter Apian at Ingolstadt expressed the same opinion, for in addition the comets of 1538 and 1539 were found to obey the same rule. If this was true for six comets it seemed highly probable that the tails of all comets are directed away from the sun —a probability which later observations eventually turned into a certainty. Here was a relationship which Aristotle, the chosen source of all physical knowledge, had overlooked, although it in no way affected belief in the meteorological nature of comets. According to Aristotle, the tails, being lighter than the heads, should be turned straight away from the earth. It also drew attention to the dominating influence of the sun and so indirectly encouraged Copernican views, and made nonsense of the astrological doctrine of the generative and directive influence of Mars, but this point appears to have been conveniently overlooked.

In November, 1572, a 'new' star* shone forth in the constellation of Cassiopeia, and observers all over Europe made hasty preparations to watch the development of what promised to be another comet. To the surprise of some, however, the star remained fixed—at least observations over many months failed to reveal any sensible parallax. Instead, it developed no tail but rose in brilliance until it rivalled Venus at its maximum splendour. By January it had fallen to about the brightness level of the brightest stars, and continued to decrease until March 1574, when it ceased to be visible. It was like a comet only in the way it appeared to come from nowhere and vanish without leaving a trace. Entirely

* A galactic supernova and by no means the first of its kind. In addition to earlier objects of this nature, novae blazed out in 945, 1054, and 1264. The Crab Nebula, recently found to be an intense radio source, is possibly the gaseous remnant of the nova of 1054. The remains of the 1572 nova have so far eluded optical detection.

different was the absence of a sensible parallax. To this there could be only one conclusion—the object was certainly above the orbit of the moon, most likely as remote as the planet Saturn, and perhaps even situated in the sphere of fixed stars. In any case there was something wrong with Aristotelian teaching, for this denied change and corruption beyond the sphere of the moon.

Tycho Brahe, a young Danish nobleman, saw the star on the evening of November 11, 1572, when he was returning home for supper and happened to look up at the sky. He was familiar with the stars overhead, and was so surprised at seeing this bright intruder that he asked his attendants and passers-by whether they, too, could see it. He was then living at Heridsvad Abbey, about twenty miles from Helsingbord in Denmark, and spent many fruitless hours in attempts to turn base metals into gold. Astrology was then his ruling passion, and he loved its practical aspects whether they involved making instruments for astronomical observations or using crucibles and furnaces in alchemical procedures. Full of ideas as to the possible astrological significance of the new star, the practically minded astrologer–astronomer observed it regularly over the following months, measuring its position and meridian altitudes with a well-made sextant of walnut wood and about $5\frac{1}{2}$ feet in radius. Despite reports to the contrary from other observers, Tycho was unable to detect any movement of the new star relative to the familiar stars of the W of Cassiopeia. He naturally concluded that it was not a comet but a new body of immense size generated in the aetherial regions of the highest heaven.

The fact that observers could not agree among themselves whether the star showed perceptible movement or not had a most stimulating effect on practical astronomy. All manner of sighting devices were directed heavenwards, often with more zeal than accuracy, and eyes were strained again and again in the hope of proving or disproving what others had found. At his country residence near Augsburg, Paul Hainzel trained an immense 19-foot oak quadrant on the star. Tycho had planned and designed this instrument, and he heard with satisfaction that Hainzel's findings confirmed his own. At Cassel, Landgrave Wilhelm IV retired to his observatory to bring clocks and graduated instruments into service. He was the first to use meridian transit methods for determining star positions, and by such means considered that the star showed a small but definite parallax. Caspar Peucer and Wolfgang Schüler at Wittenberg procured an old wooden quadrant, found a parallax of 19 minutes, and later reduced it almost to zero when they used a large and new triquetrum. Thaddaeus Hagecius, physician to the Emperor Maximilian II at Prague, obtained a number of conflicting but small values for the parallax, as did Thomas Digges in England with his cross-staff. Michael Maestlin at Tübingen possessed no instruments and merely estimated the star's position relative to a thread which he aligned relative to four neighbouring stars. He concluded that it had no appreciable parallax—an observation which Digges confirmed when he adopted a similar method. Elias Camerarius, on the other hand, first found a parallax of 12 minutes and later one of 4½ minutes from which he concluded that the object had receded in a straight line, and therefore suffered a diminution in brightness.

Whilst the new or temporary star demonstrated to a few of the more advanced astronomers that change and decay can occur among the stars, it did not particularly encourage the idea of a moving earth. The above-mentioned observers were content merely to attempt to determine the parallax from observations made during a single night (the daily parallax). Digges, on the other hand, hoped to test the Copernican theory by comparing observations separated in time by about six months. If the object was just beyond the orbit of Saturn, the earth in this period would have traversed an effective 'base line' equal to the diameter of its orbit and large enough to give the star a measurable parallax (the annual parallax). Digges was disappointed at the null result, although it did not stop him from continuing to explain and defend the Copernican system. He was not to know that the explanation lay not in any shortcomings in the Copernican theory, but in the crude instruments at his disposal. It was not until 1838 that the first annual stellar parallax, and hence the distance of a star, was measured. The star was 61 Cygni, and its parallax came to a mere fraction of a second of arc.

On November 11, 1577, Tycho saw a comet with a long tail, but cloudy skies prevented measurements of its size and position until the night of the 13th. Tycho had just moved to Hveen, a small island in the Danish Sound and some fourteen miles to the north of Copenhagen. The generosity of King Frederick II had made him its owner and the possessor of a palatial observatory, which under the name *Uraniborg* was at once a self-contained scientific establishment and a private residence. Here Tycho began to assemble what eventually became a princely collection of large graduated instruments, and for nearly twenty years gave most of them regular employment. With their aid he and his assistants advanced observational astronomy to a stage far beyond that ever achieved by the Arabians and even by Ulugh Bey at Samarcand.

At the time of the appearance of the comet of 1577, Tycho had to depend largely on the 5½-foot sextant, and this showed that the parallax was less than a third of a degree. The tail was at first 22° in length, but it grew shorter and fainter as the weeks went by, and in the following January could scarcely be seen. Tycho considered that it pointed more towards Venus than towards the sun,* although by no means away from the earth as Aristotle had supposed. He plotted the course of the head with such accuracy that astronomers in later times were able to derive its orbit in space, but he himself was content to ascribe it an irregular motion in a circular although perhaps slightly elliptical orbit. This path he placed outside that of the moon, and also that of Venus on the Copernican theory (which, incidentally, he did not support). For the first time, and despite its irregular motion a comet was assigned to a definite orbit and almost given a planetary status.

Jerome Cardan had discussed the physical nature of comets, and like him, Tycho believed that their 'heads' were neither so

---

* The tail did in fact deviate about 21° from the radius vector.

dense as to reflect sunlight fully as does the moon, nor so rare as to transmit it freely. The porous head of the visitor of 1577 therefore gave passage to some of the sunbeams which appeared to stream out from behind it like a beard or tail. This would account, he thought, for the fact that stars could be seen through the tail. His calculations, furthermore, showed that the head was at least as large as one-thirtieth of the volume of the earth, and the tail reached a maximum length of some 70,000 German miles. He concluded that although it appeared small in the sky, the comet was a tremendous object and was independent of terrestrial influences in regard to both its nature and motion.

Like the temporary star or nova of 1572, the comet gave rise to considerable speculation, but comparatively little accurate observation. A great outpouring of pamphlets and tracts of an astrological nature appeared, for few astronomers were interested in the comet for its own sake. Tycho also discussed its astrological significance, but he did at least subject it to as thorough a scientific examination as was then possible. Two of those who possessed something of his enthusiasm for practical work failed to take parallax measurements; Paul Hainzel's great quadrant lay broken after a great storm had felled it in December 1574, and the Landgrave Wilhelm IV possessed no Court astronomer. The Landgrave wrote that he believed the comet to be supra-lunar, an opinion in which he was joined by Maestlin and Cornelius Gemma, a physician of Louvain. The majority, with Hagecius as its best representative, still believed that the comet was generated in the upper atmosphere.

Those who thought little of astronomy and still less of the nova and comet appear to have been the most bombastic in their oracular pronouncements. In the light of the severe religious teachings of the time the nova was likened to the Star of Bethlehem, and the comet to a rod of correction. Some preachers urged their flocks to heed these Divine warnings and to live more godly lives, others told of future burnings and heresies and diffused a spirit of repentance and panic. The comet, said one, was a celestial prophet sent by God to encourage religious exercises and brotherly love. Another stated that it owed its generation to the sins of the world which rose to heaven and were kindled by the wrath of God. In its course over Europe the comet would shed pestilence and poison over degenerate mankind; only through prayers, psalms, and processions of penitence could the faithful hope to divert God's anger on to unbelievers. The wisest taught that He alone knew what the comet signified—that it was fruitless to assign either causes or consequences. As Luther had himself said: 'What God wills is right not because He ought so to will; but what takes place is right because He so wills. For the will of the creature a cause or reason may be laid down, but not for the will of the Creator, else you must set over Him another creator.'

Whilst preachers seasoned sermons and discourses in this way, astrologers ransacked past history for further examples of strange sights in the heavens. They, too, had the public thinking in terms of disaster, for wars, pestilences, and the fall of cities had been so frequent that it was difficult to find a comet which had heralded peace. Some failed to distinguish between a nova and a comet, others thought that the nova was another Star of Bethlehem which this time indicated Christ's second coming and the terrors of the Apocalypse. The majority concerned themselves with the comet, which they believed was influenced by either Mars and Saturn, or Mars and Venus. Those of the former persuasion predicted drought, fire, and bloodshed; those of the latter, and especially English astrologers under the rule of Queen Elizabeth, spoke of the advancement and importance of women. Despite his earlier enthusiasm for astrology, Tycho wrote about the importance of the nova, but said little to nothing about the comet's influence. It was not that he no longer doubted the value of astrology, but rather that he placed little reliance on predictions made with inaccurate planetary tables. In addition, he was finding that astronomy was worth studying as an end in itself rather than as a means to an end—an attitude which was then almost unique.

Tycho was no convert to the Copernican theory. Instead, he

introduced yet another system which conveniently agreed with
the mathematical, physical, and religious principles of the times.
He considered his failure to detect any annual parallax for the
fixed stars, coupled with his belief that they not only subtended
angles of two or three minutes but were at no great distance beyond Saturn's orbit, was a decisive argument against the heliocentric doctrine. He could not accept the vast empty space which
Copernicus had placed between Saturn and the stars. It was, he
thought, entirely wasteful, and it meant for him that the brightest
stars were incredibly large. He also advanced the argument that so
heavy a body as 'the gross, slothful body of the Earth' could not
possibly possess motion. 'I think then', he adds, 'that we must
decidedly and without doubt place the earth immovable in the
centre of the world, according to the belief of the ancients and the
testimony of Scripture.'

Tycho's system, published in 1588, was an ingenious compromise between the Copernican and Ptolemaic views of the
universe; the five planets encircled the sun, 'the chief and king',
which in turn revolved like the moon about a stationary and non-
rotating earth. The orbits of Mercury and Venus had radii smaller
than that of the solar orbit; those of Mars, Jupiter, and Saturn
encircled the earth. The smallest orbit was that of the moon, its
radius being twenty-six times the diameter of the earth; the sun
was some twenty times and Saturn 235 times more distant than
the moon. Although he spent the rest of his life making systematic
observations to this end, Tycho made little progress with the
details of his system. With the addition of appropriate epicycles
and eccentric circles it would have proved mathematically equivalent to the Copernican system.

Tycho's work at Uraniborg marked the culmination of pre-
telescopic astronomy. His instrumental equipment was the largest
and finest in the world, his measurements surpassed all others in
accuracy, and his example established the disciplines of systematic
observation in practical astronomy. With unsparing energy and
trouble he and his assistants investigated the errors of their in-

struments and the motions of the sun, moon, and planets. They also drew up an entirely new catalogue of 777 stars (later increased to 1,004), using the modern equatorial system of right ascension and declination, and not, as formerly, celestial latitude and longitude. As the star places were fixed they were marked on a great 5-foot globe suitably embellished with the constellation figures. Out of all this work came the final break with the crystalline spheres of Aristotle, the complete rejection of *trepidation*, and the first investigations into the effects of astronomical refraction. Also from it, and within the comparatively narrow compass of twenty years, came the discovery of the *variation* (see p. 134) and *annual equation*, two inequalities of the moon's motion, the fluctuation in the inclination of the moon's orbit to the ecliptic, and tables of the sun's motion superior by far to those given in the *Alfonsine* and *Prutenic* Tables.

In 1588 the death of King Frederick robbed Tycho of the support of his one really appreciative patron. His successor and son, Christian, was but a boy at the time, and Tycho's enemies began to follow up their advantage. Tycho had always been self-willed and imperious by nature, and the troubles which beset him after 1588 appear to have been largely of his own making. He had quarrels with pupils and with his tenants on Hveen and other estates. In 1596, when Christian was crowned King Christian IV, Tycho's detractors really went to work. His allowances were reduced and then withdrawn, and finally even his pension was stopped. He was made to feel that his work was no longer wanted, and in rage and mortification he left Hveen for good, taking his instruments, chemical apparatus, and printing press with him. Ten years of uncertainty followed, with temporary residences at Copenhagen, Rostock, Wandsbeck, and Wittenberg, but in June 1599 he arrived at Prague, ready and willing to enter the service of the liberal but eccentric German Emperor Rudolph II. Here he resumed his observations, but on a much-restricted scale, and early in the following year had his first meeting with Johannes Kepler.

Kepler had studied astronomy at the Protestant University of

Tübingen under Maestlin, from whom he derived a deep and abiding belief in the truth of the Copernican system. At Tycho's new residence at the Castle of Benatky, some twenty-two miles from Prague, Kepler participated in the observing programme and worked on the motions of Mercury, Venus, and Mars in readiness for new tables to be known as the *Rudolphine Tables*. On October 24, 1601, and after a short illness, Tycho died at the comparatively early age of fifty-five. On his death-bed he begged Kepler to proceed with the proposed tables and expressed the hope that he would do so according to the principles of the Tychonic system.

For eight years Kepler laboured unceasingly on the reduction of Tycho's observations of the planet Mars. For eight years he pursued the possibilities of circles and arrays of circles, but none gave motions which demonstrated the phenomena revealed by Tycho's measurements. At last, in 1609, when he had dispensed with circles altogether, he tried an oval and then an ellipse. The last, to his great joy, fitted the observations exactly and led directly to two laws of planetary motion, first, that the planet describes an ellipse, the sun being at one focus, and second, that the straight line drawn from the planet to the sun sweeps out equal areas in equal intervals of time. Deeply influenced by Pythagorean and Platonic number mysticism, and convinced that the universe is a harmonious structure pervaded by mathematical law, Kepler inferred that all the planets, the earth included, move in ellipses. For a further nine years, and despite teaching duties at Linz, family troubles, and official work in astrology for the Emperor Rudolph and his less enthusiastic successor, Matthias, Kepler pursued his quest for further numerical relationships in the solar system. The strong mystical elements in his nature led him to consider numerous fanciful analogies, as for instance one between the proportions of the planetary distances and various musical scales (see p. 54). Yet out of this immense outpouring of effort came success, for in 1618 Kepler discovered the third law of elliptical motion, namely, that the squares of the periodic times which the planets take to describe their orbits are proportional to the cubes of their mean distances from the sun. Thus it transpired that the spirit of Pythagoras and Plato, working through the concentrated efforts of Kepler, reduced the whole ancient system of component circles to seven ellipses; the break with Ptolemy was complete.

CHAPTER XIII

UNIVERSAL LAW

*He [Newton] has so clearly laid open and set
before our eyes the most beautiful frame of the
System of the World, that if King Alphonso
were now alive, he would not complain for want of
the graces either of simplicity or of harmony in it.*
                                        Roger Cotes

KEPLER once said that he contemplated the beauty of the Copernican system 'with incredible and ravishing delight'. Specially
attractive was the thought that the sun, a kind of *World Soul*, took
over the functions of the Primum Mobile, directing the planets in
their courses and extending its influence outwards to the distant
stars. By its nature, size, and position it was the one heavenly
body 'which alone we should judge to be worthy of the most high
God, if He should be pleased with a material domicile, and choose
a place in which to dwell with the blessed angels'. Kepler's joy
therefore knew no bounds when he heard that Galileo Galilei,
professor of mathematics at Padua, had turned telescopes sky-
wards and amply verified several of the physical bases of Copernicanism.

In May 1609 Galileo heard from a friend in Paris that a Dutch
spectacle-maker had so combined a pair of lenses as to magnify
distant objects. The inventor proved to be Hans Lippershey of
Middelburg in Zeeland, whose interest in financial gain prevented
him from appreciating the telescope's astronomical potentialities.
Galileo remedied this deficiency, and with his own instruments
saw evident signs that the heavenly bodies were far less divine and
perfect than the traditional Aristotelian view suggested. He saw

the disks of the planets and shadows cast by mountains on the moon, resolved the Milky Way into a vast multitude of separate stars, and observed the four major moons of Jupiter and the phases of Venus.

The Church was at first most favourably disposed towards Galileo, who travelled to Rome in the spring of 1611, exhibited his telescopes and appearances through them to cardinals and other learned men, and had a long and satisfactory audience with Pope Paul V. In June of the same year he observed that the sun's face had spots. Their changing appearances demonstrated the sun's axial rotation and straightway implied its imperfection. Galileo's enemies now felt that his madness had gone far enough; he was accused of circulating opinions contrary to the authority of Aristotle and the doctrines of Holy Scripture, and the dreaded word 'heresy' was heard in these connections. In 1616 he was again in Rome, but this time to receive a warning from the authorities neither to defend nor hold the notions of the central position of the sun and the double motion of the earth. Thereafter we find him steering a somewhat slippery course between the views of ecclesiastical authority, the decree of 1616, and his own religious beliefs and scientific findings. He embraced the Copernican side, 'proceeding as with a pure mathematical hypothesis and striving by every artifice to represent it as superior to supposing the Earth motionless'. At the same time he wished to witness to 'the salutary effect' of the decree, which 'imposed a seasonable silence upon the Pythagorean opinion that the Earth moves'. He was a devout and sincere Catholic; the world should know that Rome is not only the source of 'dogmas for the welfare of the soul', but also of 'ingenious discussion for the delight of the mind'.

In trying to meet these criteria Galileo was, of course, attempting the impossible, and in his optimism he was interpreting the decree as an admonition rather than as a prohibition. In 1623 he published *Il Saggiatore*, in which he stated that the earth's motion was 'most false' and yet managed to introduce several thinly-veiled pleas for Copernicanism. The new Pope, Urban VIII, had been pleased to give his name to the dedication, had pages read to him at meal-times, and felt kindly disposed towards the author. Galileo might well have thought that he had triumphed over his enemies—that the decree had grown favourably dim in ecclesiastical memories. In 1632 there followed his famous *Dialogo dei Massimi Sistemi* . . . or *Dialogue Concerning the Two Chief World Systems* . . ., the MS of which he submitted to the papal censors for approval. Yet despite a few changes to the text made at their request, the case for Copernicanism shone never so brightly. The work was published and proved an immediate success. Too late the censors realized their mistake; they recalled the details of the decree, interpreted the admonition as a prohibition, and charged Galileo with having practised deliberate deceit.

In 1632 Galileo was summoned to Rome, brought before the Inquisition (in 1633), and convicted 'of believing and holding the doctrines—false and contrary to the Holy and Divine Scriptures —that the sun is the centre of the world, and that it does not move from east to west, and that the earth does move and is not the centre of the world; also that an opinion can be held and supported as probable after it has been declared and decreed contrary to the Holy Scriptures'. In punishment he had to recant on his knees— to 'abjure, curse, and detest the aforesaid errors'—and to undergo virtual imprisonment in his country villa at Arcetri, near Florence.

For nine years at Arcetri, and until his death in 1642, Galileo was troubled by the surveillance of the officers of the Inquisition, failing health, and increasing blindness. Here he summed up and completed his discoveries in mechanics, thereby opening the way for Newton's great work on the mechanism of the universe. It is not without significance for science that Galileo died in 1642, the same year in which Newton was born.

Although he was once invited to teach at Bologna, Kepler wisely remained outside the pale of Roman influence. Yet even in Protestant Germany his liberal religious views offended the intolerant Lutheran authorities at Württemberg and caused him much unhappiness. Branded as a sly Calvinist and promulgator of heterodox beliefs which might undermine the faith of students, he was debarred from teaching at his old university, Tübingen, and also from participating in the celebration of Holy Communion. His one wish was to be left free to pursue his studies on a stable income which would keep himself and his growing family above want. The wish never materialized. In 1611, and against the tumultuous political and military background of the opening stages of the Thirty Years War, he lost his wife and six-year-old son. With two motherless children on his hands he married again in 1613, and eventually found himself supporting five more children of his own and the two children of his irresponsible brother Heinrich. Hence he had to support a wife and nine children in unsettled times on a salary which was inadequate and invariably paid in arrears—and sometimes not at all. In 1615 his aged mother, whom he calls 'a wild and chattering woman', was accused of witchcraft. His efforts on her behalf were unsparing, and her final acquittal at Württemberg after the proceedings of five weary years was due solely to his strong defence in her favour. To complete his store of trouble, Duke Maximilian of Bavaria stormed and reduced Linz in 1620 and straightway set about persecuting the Protestants. Finding life there more and more intolerable, Kepler moved his family to Regensburg and continued alone to search for a permanent and peaceful home. At the same time he attempted to recover various arrears in his salary, but without success. He travelled and worked at various centres in both northern and southern Germany, but the search for a satisfactory domicile proved fruitless. Worn out in body and mind he came to Regensburg in 1630, and after a short illness died there on November 15.

Among Kepler's many published works was the *Astronomiae pars Optica* (1604), a treatise on optics considered in relation to astronomy and a prelude to his more important *Dioptrice*, 1611. In the latter he discussed the optical principles of vision and showed how the refracting elements of the human eye work together to form an image of distant objects on the receiving screen of the retina. He also investigated the optics of Galileo's telescopes and designed a new type of refracting telescope which consisted of two separated convex lenses. Unlike Galileo, he did not use the telescope for furthering astronomical observation, and once confessed that 'for observations his eye was dull and for mechanical operations, his hand was awkward'.

The monumental *Rudolphine Tables*, dedicated nominally by the heirs of Tycho Brahe to the victorious Emperor Ferdinand II, were published at Ulm in 1627. As was to be expected, they gave astronomers the means to predict future events in the heavens with greater accuracy than ever before. From the tables it was apparent that both Mercury and Venus would traverse the sun's disk in 1631, the former on November 7 and the latter on December 6. Using a small telescope, Pierre Gassendi of Dique in Provence observed the transit of Mercury on the very day predicted by Kepler, although a little earlier than was expected. 'I have been more fortunate', he proudly writes, 'than those hunters after Mercury who have sought the cunning god in the sun; I found him out, and saw him where no one else had hitherto seen him.' Mercury continued to be an elusive planet both in regard to its motion and because of its proximity to the sun. Goad, who in 1686 published a large volume of astro-meteorological nonsense, calls the planet a 'squirting lacquey of the sun, who seldom shows his head in these parts, as if he was in debt'. Such was the low level to which the messenger of the gods had fallen in the eyes of one mystic at least!

Gassendi also kept watch for the transit of Venus, and anticipating the possibility that the calculated time might be too late, began observations on December 4. This time he was unsuccessful, but owing to the fact that the transit took place when the sun was not visible from France—that is, on the night of December 6. The next transit of Venus, on November 24, 1639, was predicted and observed by Jeremiah Horrox, a young English clergyman.

Galileo failed to appreciate Kepler's work on planetary motions, and in this connection pinned his faith on uniform velocities in circular orbits. For both astronomers, the starry vault of heaven, although incredibly remote, was spherical and sun-centred. Other ideas, however, were afoot—ideas which led eventually to the realization that the sun is a star, howbeit the nearest one, in a vast concourse of stars which forms the stellar system. One of the first to suggest that the stars are distributed in depth to almost infinite distances was Giordano Bruno, a fiery and imaginative monk of Nola, near Naples. An admirer of the teachings of Nicholas Cusanus and Copernicus, Bruno led the life of a wandering scholar, disputing and quarrelling in the capitals of Europe, London included. Among other heretical doctrines he taught the idea of the plurality of worlds, believing that an infinite number of stars populate infinite space and that these stars are suns which have families of inhabited planets. More than anything else his exuberant pantheism made people consider cosmological issues and question authority. He stood for freedom of thought, and this was his downfall, for, returning to Italy in 1592, he was seized by the Roman Inquisition, and eight years later was burnt alive on the Campo dei Fiori in Rome.

Bruno resided in England between the years 1583 and 1585, so that his ideas were perhaps influenced by an important and popular treatise which Thomas Digges published in 1576. Digges, as we have already seen, was an ardent Copernican, and in his treatise he made the idea of an infinite number of stars a logical corollary to the Copernican system. 'This orbe of starres fixed infinitely up,' he writes, 'extendeth itself in altitude sphericallye, and therefore immovable the pallace of foelicitye garnished with perpetuall shininge glorious lightes innumerable, farr excellinge our sonne both in quantitye and qualitye.'

Further breaks with the Aristotelian tradition of an immense, single, and unchanging sphere of fixed stars were made by the discovery of two important variable stars and the appearance of a spectacular nova. In 1596 Fabricius saw what he took to be a new star in the neck of the Whale (*Cetus*). The star was then of the third magnitude, but after two months it had slowly fallen into invisibility and was not seen again until 1637. Catalogued as o *Ceti* by Bayer in 1605, and often referred to as *Mira*, the Wonderful, it was later found to be a variable star—that is, to rise and fall in brightness with a mean period of about 360 days. Although it was therefore never extinguished, its faintness at minimum, coupled with the fact that its low meridian altitude puts it above the horizon for rather less than twelve hours, tended to conceal its periodicity. Another variable, a star designated P *Cygni* and situated in the neck of the Swan, was discovered in 1600 by William Jansen. It was then of the third magnitude, and stood at about this brightness when Kepler saw it two years later. In 1621 it was invisible to the eye, but regained its former lustre during 1657 to 1659, only to vanish again in 1660. After further changes it fell to about the fifth magnitude, and has remained at this level ever since. The most striking celestial event, however, occurred in September 1604, when a hitherto unrecorded faint star * blazed out in the constellation of *Ophiuchus*. It was studied by Kepler, Maestlin, and others, rose almost to rival Venus in splendour, and then gradually diminished until it disappeared early in 1606. Attempts to determine its parallax proved fruitless; like the nova of 1572 it was clearly another example of change in the highest heaven.

Old and deep-rooted traditions die hard, especially when bolstered by the dictates of authority. In the case of the heliocentric theory its upholders had to reckon with the dogmas of theology, enforced in Catholic countries by the strong arm of the Inquisition which had burnt Bruno and browbeaten Galileo. To make matters worse, *De Revolutionibus*, Galileo's *Dialogo*, and Kepler's *Epitome of the Copernican Astronomy* had been put on the papal *Index of Prohibited Books* and remained there until as late as 1821.

In England after the reign of Mary, and in the freer intellectual atmosphere of Protestantism, the heliocentric theory found more supporters than detractors. Foremost among the latter was Francis Bacon, advocate of the method of induction in science, and therefore a staunch believer in the value of experimental procedures.

* Another galactic supernova, the remnants of which constitute an intense radio source.

He felt, and perhaps not unreasonably, that more evidence was wanted on the physical side—evidence to prove beyond all doubt that the earth is both rotating and speeding about the sun at some sixteen miles per second. Even in 1622, and when any Englishman with a telescope and good vision could test all Galileo's observations for himself, Bacon still regarded Copernicanism as a purely speculative system, introduced by one 'who cares not what fictions he introduces into nature, provided his calculations answer'. Likewise the Greek view of uniform and circular motions among the planets was 'feigned and assumed for ease and advantage of calculation'. For Bacon the laws which reign in the heavens are no different from those which operate on the earth; the Aristotelian view that the heat of the sun is a different thing from the heat of a coal fire, is he declares, 'deliberately designed to cripple enterprise'.

Similar ideas were also held by William Gilbert, physician-in-ordinary to Elizabeth and James I, who in 1600 summed up current knowledge regarding magnetism and static electricity in his famous *De Magnete*. He made numerous experiments with lodestones and compass needles, and explained why the latter, when freely suspended, dip through an angle depending on the latitude. He also showed that many old beliefs (like that which told of mountains so strongly magnetic as to draw out the nails from passing ships) were no more than old wives' tales. The earth, he concluded, not only behaves like an immense magnet, but is actually made out of lodestone except for a superficial covering of rocks, water, and soil. By reason of its magnetic soul or spirit, therefore, the earth spins on its axis, keeps itself together, and can extend its influence up to the heavens. Similarly, the interacting magnetic virtues of the planets give rise to their motions and determine the order of the cosmos. Magnetism for Gilbert was what gravity became for Newton and his followers—the bond and mainstay of the physical universe.

By giving the earth magnetic poles, Gilbert was able to explain why pivoted compass needles tend to point to the north. This was a complete break with traditional views, for, as he says, 'The common herd of philosophizers, in search of the causes of magnetic movements, called in causes remote and far away.' One investigator had suggested that a discrete magnetic influence existed beyond the highest heaven, Peter the Pilgrim thought it resided at the celestial poles, and Cardan ascribed it 'to the star in the tail of *Ursa Major'*. The names 'lode-star' and 'stella maris' applied by early seamen to the Pole Star likewise witnesses to this supposed connection. 'So has ever been the wont of mankind,' Gilbert complains; 'homely things are vile; things from abroad and things afar are dear to them and the object of longing.'

Gilbert failed to notice that the compass needle does not always point north and south, but makes an angle with the meridian which is variable in amount both for one place and for different places at one and the same time. The geographical variation of magnetic declination, revealed to Columbus on his memorable voyage of 1492, was first plotted on charts (called *isogonic* maps) by Halley after long voyages on the Atlantic and Pacific Oceans.

In contrast to the views of Bacon, and in a lesser extent to those of Gilbert, was the keen Copernican spirit of men like Bourne, Digges, Blagrave, Ridley, and others—men who through their textbooks and popular writings did much to educate the lettered public in the practical applications of mathematics. So effective was their united contribution, and so great the interest shown in Galileo's discoveries, that English scientists after about 1620 completely abandoned the outworn Ptolemaic theory.

One outstanding problem remained—the detection of stellar parallax. Using instruments of greater power and accuracy than those used by Tycho, and assisted by the application of telescopic sights, successive generations of astronomers attacked this problem, and in so doing, brought to light effects no less important. First in time, if not in importance, was Halley's suspicion, expressed in 1718, that certain stars have proper motions relative to the rest. By comparing early Alexandrian observations recorded by Ptolemy with those of his own times, Halley inferred that the stars *Aldebaran, Arcturus,* and *Sirius* were moving slowly towards the celestial equator. This conjecture regarding three stars naturally invited suspicions as to the fixity of the rest and indirectly made Digges' idea of stars arranged in depth more palatable. At the close of 1725, and whilst attempting to detect stellar parallax with a zenith telescope erected at Kew, James Bradley detected changes in the apparent position of the star γ *Draconis*. These and other observations, continued over the following years, led to the discovery, not of parallax, but to a hitherto unknown effect known as aberration. Bradley rightly judged it to be due to the finite velocity of light relative to the velocity of the earth in its orbit, thereby demonstrating in a completely new and independent way the manner and extent of the earth's motion. Since Ole Roemer in 1675, and from observations of the satellites of Jupiter, had obtained a reasonable value for the velocity of light (141,000 miles/sec. as compared with the present day value of just over 186,000 miles/sec.), Bradley was able to calculate the earth's orbital velocity. About fifty years later, and again with a view to detecting stellar parallax, William Herschel began to study double stars. Using large reflecting telescopes of his own manufacture he discovered several thousand of these objects, and in 1803 announced that many of them form independent systems, each pair revolving about their common centre of gravity under the influence of their mutual attraction. The secret of a star's distance was first resolved in 1838, when the German astronomer Friedrich W. Bessel published the results of his measurements of the star 61 *Cygni*. Its distance came out at about half a million times that of sun from the earth—and yet it is one of the sun's nearest neighbours!

As observational and mathematical astronomy advanced, interest in astrology waned. The picture of a sun-centred system of planets subject to physical laws and set amidst moving stars shook men's faith in spiritual agencies and astral influences. No longer was the earth regarded as the lowly but central feature of creation, no longer did higher or purer celestial spheres control the motions of those below—indeed the very terms 'up' and 'down' lost their old cosmological significance. The status of the earth was reduced to that of the other planets—it was no longer unique in form or by nature. 'The earth's motion', Galileo had written, 'is performed with as little labour as the motion of other heavenly bodies, neither is it inferior in dignity to some of these.' Nearly two centuries later, William Herschel was demonstrating that the sun and solar system are travelling through space among the stars.

Kepler practised astrology, but mainly because this activity was often his sole means of livelihood. Galileo in his youth studied it, but only to conform to the medical curriculum at the university of Padua. Bacon considered it was 'so full of superstition that scarce anything sound can be discovered in it'. Purge it of divination and auguries, subject it to experiment and more precise observation, strip from it the doctrine of horoscopes and 'other darling inventions . . . which have kept revel, as it were, in the heavens' and it might, he thought, yield useful results.

With the growing disbelief in astrology came the weakening of its long association with alchemy. It became evident that metals do not grow from seeds in the earth, and that stones and minerals are dead, inert things unaffected by the supposed generative effects of the sun, moon, and planets. Throughout the Middle Ages, alchemy was at once a science, a philosophy, and a religious cult. Burdened with obscurantism and incongruities it could make little effective contribution to the advancing tide of Renaissance knowledge. Alchemists in the sixteenth century, and despite their sustained enthusiasm and excessive labour, failed to make gold and transmute the elements. Some became so absorbed in their work, that like the great Belgian chemist J. B. van Helmont, who believed that he had turned mercury into gold, they seldom stirred outdoors. Others hid their failures in trickery, and when they were exposed, brought themselves and the Hermetic Art into disrepute. Indeed, it was not until alchemists forsook the quest for gold, the elixir of life, and the universal solvent, that they began to make contributions of positive value to science. Paracelsus, as we have seen, applied chemistry to medicine; the German physician Georg Agricola described mining and metallurgical processes; van Helmont wrote an important textbook (*Alchemia*, 1597), planned chemical laboratories, and became interested in gases. But the first real break with the old traditions came in the seventeenth century, and at the hands of Robert Boyle, often called 'the father of modern chemistry'.

In London and Oxford, and whilst still a young man, Boyle came under the influence of several of the members of the newly-formed Invisible College, later the Royal Society. Like Newton, he was an ardent alchemist, but he nevertheless felt that it should be studied in its own right and not necessarily as the handmaid of medicine or the key to making gold. The theories of the alchemists he found to be like peacock's feathers—they 'make a great show, but are neither solid nor useful'. He was therefore tempted to see whether he could 'do anything towards the repairing of it by handling Chymistry, not as a Physician, or an Alchymist, but as a meer Naturalist, and so by applying Chymical Operations to Philosophical purposes'. The result was a number of important experimental contributions to both physics and chemistry, and besides other publications, his great work *The Sceptical Chymist*, first published in 1661. In this book he dispensed with the four 'elements' of Aristotle, the 'souls', 'spirits', and 'principles' of the Arabian alchemists, and the *tria prima* of Paracelsus. Instead, he wrote about atoms and elements, made a study of combustion, and investigated the properties of air—laying thereby the bases of modern ideas in physics and chemistry. Alchemical traditions lingered until well into the eighteenth century, but the long age of alchemy virtually ended with the work of Boyle.

The year of the publication of *De Revolutionibus*, 1543, saw also the appearance of another impressive book, the *De Humani Corporis Fabrica* (*Fabric of the Human Body*), by Andreas Vesalius. Whereas Copernicus had reordered the motions of the heavens, Vesalius at Padua reconstructed the anatomy of man. In those days medical teaching, based on the works of Galen and leading

Arabians like Avicenna and Rhazes, saw little original investigation. As the professor of anatomy read extracts from Galen, his students gathered round an opened cadaver and watched the demonstrator as he pointed out the various parts with a wand. Vesalius, in direct contrast, performed his own dissections and described the internal organs as he himself saw them. Authority, he felt, should give way to precise observation and experiment. Yet, like Copernicus, he was too steeped in tradition to break completely with the past. Hence he mixed human with animal anatomy, laid bare the circulatory system without understanding its mechanism, and although he uncovered over two hundred errors of Galenism, he left many more uncorrected. His was the first real break with medical orthodoxy, and as was to be expected, his book aroused considerable opposition. He eventually abandoned research, became Court physician to the Emperor Charles V, and died whilst on a penitential pilgrimage to the Holy Land.

The problem of the circulation of the blood again received attention at the hands of Miguel Servetus, a versatile Spanish theologian and physician notorious for his heretical views on Original Sin and the Trinity. These he published in 1553, together with a short passage which makes it clear that he had somehow discovered the lesser circulation—that he knew that venous blood enters the lungs, mixes with the air, and returns to the heart as bright arterial blood. These physiological subtleties, however, were lost on Calvin, his mortal enemy. He was arrested on the charge of Arianism, imprisoned, and promptly brought to justice. In October 1553, wearing a crown of straw and with his book bound to his side, Servetus was chained to a stake and burned alive in Champel Place, Geneva, 'to furnish an example to others who might wish to commit the like'.

The Galenic idea of the ebb and flow of the blood persisted until the time of William Harvey, himself a student under Fabricius and an admirer of the works of Aristotle and Galen. Harvey published his account of the circulation in 1628, dedicating his book to Charles I whom he calls 'the sun of the world around him, the heart of the republic'. By controlled experiments and close observation guided by the theory that 'the movement of the blood is constantly in a circle', he showed how the rhythmic movement of the muscular heart maintained the circulatory flow of a given volume of blood. This revolutionary idea naturally met with violent criticism in conservative quarters, but he had the support of the fellows of the Royal Society (established in 1660 but initiated about fifteen years earlier), and lived to see his discovery generally adopted. By 1657, the year of Harvey's death, Willis, Sydenham, Ray, Grew, Boyle, Hooke, and Lower were following his precept 'to search out and to study the secrets of Nature by way of experiment'. Before the century was out, Malpighi observed the capillary vessels through a microscope and thereby completed the story of the circulation.

The seventeenth century saw also the temporary enthronement of Cartesian philosophy, the mechanical ideas of which were opposed to Aristotle's vitalism and the teleological utterances of Galen. For René Descartes, the physical universe, no less than the human body, was a machine made by the hand of God, and as such was subject to the laws of statics and dynamics. With Descartes came the dichotomy between mind and matter; animals were mere automata, but *l'homme-machine* housed a material soul in the pineal body. Cartesianism led to a renewed interest in scientific anatomy and fostered another line of medical inquiry—the physiology of respiration, an outgrowth of the crumbling structure of alchemy.

With the gradual if faltering rise of scientific medicine, medical astrology, having nothing of value to contribute, slowly dropped into well-merited obscurity. It became increasingly evident that the moon and planets have no jurisdiction whatever over the natural processes in man. The results of bleeding were found to be beneficial or otherwise irrespective of the phase of the moon, and patients responded to Hippocratic treatments despite the unfavourable aspects of dominating stars in their horoscopes. Astrology sometimes entered the medical arena when all else failed, as when the astrologer Lilly was questioned at the House of Commons by a special committee appointed to inquire into the causes of the great plague and fire of London. Lilly said that his calculations had warned him of the city's double affliction, but that he had not foreseen the year. He concluded that it was 'the finger of God only' and admitted ignorance as to 'what instruments He used thereunto'. In brief, and as was to be expected, the committee drew a blank from this quarter.

As long as the doctrine of humours in one form or another dictated clinical procedures, established medicine continued to be baffled as to the causes of plagues and diseases. Towards the end of the nineteenth century, however, it became evident that a complete reorientation of ideas in pathology was necessary. Much had been learnt about the processes of human physiology, and a growing body of evidence showed that parasitical micro-organisms play a large, if not dominant rôle in the balance of nature. Familiarity with the life-histories and effects of an increasing number of identifiable microbes promised control over rather than subservience to environment. The break with the humoral theory—with humoral pathology and its astrological trimmings—was as complete as it was final.

Although comets lost some of their sepulchral aspects when they came to be examined through telescopes, it was not until after Newton's and Halley's mathematical work on cometary orbits that their motions ceased to elude investigators. Tycho assigned comets to circular orbits, Galileo thought they moved in straight lines and were no more than terrestrial exhalations, Kepler considered that they pursued rectilinear paths or at least paths sensibly rectilinear. For Kepler, comets were of a temporary nature, were as numerous as fishes in the sea, and owed their genesis to impure celestial matter or a 'species of filth'. As this gross material collected into a large ball, it generated its own motion and came under the scavenging influence of the sun's penetrating rays. In this way the ball or 'head' was forced to dissipate itself, the matter driven out by the sunlight constituting the comet's tail. In support of this theory, Kepler remarked on the changes seen in the great comet of 1618, an object which the Jesuit astronomer Jean-Baptiste Cysat thought showed every tendency of breaking up. One comet, known as Biela's Comet, actually did this during its 1845–6 apparition.

Several impressive comets appeared during the seventeenth century, and in one way or another stirred public imagination into thoughts of disaster. Daniel Defoe, the author of *Robinson Crusoe*, saw the comet of 1664 which heralded the terrors of the Great Plague. He records that some thought it 'of a faint, dull, languid colour, and its motion very heavy, solemn, and slow', but warns his readers that his countrymen 'were more addicted to prophecies and astrological conjurations, dreams, and old wives' tales, than ever they were before or since'. In comparison with this object the comet of 1665–6 appeared bright and sparkling 'or, as others said, flaming, and its motion swift and furious'. 'I saw both these stars,' Defoe writes, 'and must confess I had so much the common notion of such things in my head, that I was apt to look upon them as the forerunners and warnings of God's judgements.'

On December 4, 1680, a hen at Rome laid an egg on which was imprinted the figure of the great comet of that year. 'The fact was attested by his Holiness,' writes a chronicler, 'by the Queen of Sweden, and all the persons of first quality in Rome.' The comet lasted from December 16, 1680, until the following January, and caused such widespread terror in Germany that a medal was struck to allay public fear. 'This star threatens evil things,' says the superscription; 'Only Trust! God will make things turn to good.' A more rational approach was made by Georg Doerffel, son of a German pastor of Plauen and pupil of the astronomer Hevelius, who studied its motion and concluded that it moved in a parabolic orbit with the sun in the focus. The same comet also gave rise to a special sensation some years later, for the Rev. William Whiston, successor to Newton in the chair of mathematics at Cambridge and editor of a standard edition of the works of Josephus, traced its influence back to the times of Noah and *Genesis*. Halley had erroneously ascribed a period of 575 years to the comet, and Whiston, working backwards with the assistance of history and the Scriptures, concluded that it was responsible for giving the earth its initial motion and rotation. A later close approach, he argued, had enveloped the earth in the comet's tail and given rise to the Deluge, whilst a future collision would bring about the end of the world as predicted in *Revelation*. Whiston, it need hardly be said, stood almost alone in holding these and other heterodoxies, which he voiced with such enthusiasm that in 1701 he was forced to resign from his professorship.

Observations of the comet of 1682 enabled Halley to assign it an elliptical orbit of high eccentricity and a period of about sixty-seven years. He thereupon searched past records for accounts of previous appearances, and after calculating the orbits of twenty-four comets for which the observational data seemed adequate, remarked that the comets of 1531, 1607, and 1682 were one and the same object. As we have already seen, he predicted its return for 1758, but owing to the gravitational influence of Jupiter and Saturn it did not reappear in our skies until January 1759. Thereafter comets began to lose their supernatural attributes, but the possibility of cometary collisions sustained public interest in them until as late as the present century.

Halley was one of the few astronomers of the eighteenth century who believed that shooting stars and meteorites come from outer space. In 1794, E. F. F. Chladni, a physicist of Wittenberg, wrote a book in which he suggested that certain metallic masses found in Germany and Russia were extra-terrestrial in origin. But his findings were received with considerable scepticism; the majority continued to regard meteorites as being parts of the earth's surface. Then two important events completely over-turned old ideas. The first occurred on April 26, 1803, when a large, fiery mass sped across the sky in daytime and then exploded. Thousands of hot fragments were scattered far and wide around the town of L'Aigle in Normandy. The French physicist

Biot collected and examined specimens, intercompared eye-witness accounts, and concluded that the stone came from outer space, and with so great a velocity that its outer layers were brought almost to incandescence. Even so, the origin of this and similar objects still remained a mystery, although many believed that they had been ejected by volcanoes on the earth or moon. The second event was on the night of November 14, 1833, when a sustained shower of meteors appeared to radiate from the constellation *Leo*. This magnificent spectacle was repeated in 1866 and led directly to the idea of a swarm of meteors travelling in an orbit round the sun with a period of $33\frac{1}{4}$ years. Whenever the earth passes through the main cluster in this swarm, major meteoric showers are witnessed, displays which H. A. Newton, who predicted the major shower of 1866, traced back in history to the year A.D. 902. Next in importance was Schiaparelli's discovery that the August meteors which radiate from *Perseus* move in the same orbit as the third comet of 1862, and the identification by Leverrier and Peters of the orbit of the November *Leonids* with that of Tempel's telescopic comet of 1866. Thereafter the study of meteors and of meteor streams became an important and attractive branch of astronomy.

But for improved methods of time determination, many of the seventeenth-century successes in practical and fundamental astronomy would have been impossible. Whilst still a student, Galileo had discovered the principle of the isochronism of the pendulum and had applied it for measuring the pulse rate. At a later date, and during his virtual imprisonment at Arcetri, he discussed with his son Vincenzio and pupil Viviani how a pendulum might be applied for the regulation of clock mechanisms. No clock materialized, however, so we can only assume that their efforts were fruitless. Although Joost Bürgi, clockmaker successively to the Landgrave William IV and the Emperor Rudolph II, is said to have constructed one about 1612, the invention of the pendulum clock rightly belongs to Christian Huygens, the great physicist, mathematician, and astronomer of Zulichem, Holland. Huygens regulated a clock in this way about 1655, and in 1658 published a full account of its principle and construction. After that date this type of clock quickly established itself throughout Europe as a most promising observatory clock, the more so since its audible half-second tick enabled astronomers to judge the exact moments of star transits with much greater precision than before. As a ships' chronometer, however, the pendulum clock was most disappointing, for its swinging bob was far too easily affected by the tossing of a ship.

The reader will have judged that the age-old problem of longitude determination was little nearer solution in Huygens' time than 100 years earlier. The Spanish and Dutch Governments offered substantial cash prizes to stimulate research in this problem, made the more pressing by reason of the commercial rivalry between them and the opening of new sea routes. Since the ordinary balance clock and watch could not be relied on to keep accurate time on a long sea voyage, astronomers sought alternative means for finding longitude. Galileo, for instance, suggested a method based on the eclipses of Jupiter's satellites by the body of the planet, and discussed its possibilities in correspondence with naval authorities in Spain. The idea was not adopted, however, for no accurate tables of the motions of the satellites were then available, and in any case their precise observation required using a telescope of fairly high power—no easy task from the deck of a moving ship at sea. An alternative method, originally suggested in 1514 by John Werner of Nürnberg, proved more fruitful. Based on 'lunar distances', for the measurement of angular distances of well-known stars from the moon, it required for its success both reliable tables of the moon's motion and an accurate catalogue of zodiacal stars. It was primarily to obtain these ideals that Greenwich Observatory was founded in 1675, the Rev. John Flamsteed being appointed 'to apply himself with the most exact care and diligence to the Rectifying the Tables of the Motions of the Heavens and the Places of the Fixed Stars'. At the same time it was considered advisable to encourage the horological aspects of navigation, and in 1714 the British Government began to offer prizes for a clock or watch which would have an almost constant rate despite temperature changes and the rolling of ships. The prize of £20,000 was won by John Harrison, whose historic chronometer with its temperature-compensated balance wheel kept Greenwich time correct to two minutes during a voyage across the Atlantic. Nevil Maskelyne was then Astronomer Royal, and he it was who in 1767 instituted the annual publication of the *Nautical Almanac*.

The oldest problem of all, that of obtaining a reliable calendar, found partial resolution in 1582, when Catholic countries adopted the sweeping calendrial reforms of the ageing Pope Gregory XIII. Under his patronage Luigi Lilio and Christopher Clavius spent several years working on proposals for an improved calendar, the result of which was the so-called *Gregorian* calendar of modern times. On the old Julian basis the vernal equinox in 1582 fell on March 11 instead of on March 21, its date in 325 when the Church Council met at Nicaea (see p. 169). To restore the equinox to its originally assigned date, therefore, and to ensure that Easter remained a spring festival, ten days were dropped out of the year 1582, the day following October 4 being called October 15. To keep the equinox on March 31, every year divisible by four, and every secular year divisible by four hundred (that is, 1600, 2000, etc.) was to be made a leap year of 366 days. On this basis the difference between the Gregorian year and the tropical year comes to nearly three days in 10,000 years, or only twenty-two seconds annually. At the time England and other Protestant countries thought that the reform smacked too heavily of popery, and they promptly rejected it, despite the fact that Roger Bacon, Dee, and others had already made similar proposals. Dee apparently convinced Elizabeth that the change was worth adopting, and a Bill was in fact presented to Parliament in 1585 to this effect, but it got no further than a second reading.

Another valuable calendrial contribution, likewise introduced in 1582, was Joseph Scaliger's 'Julian Period'. This was an attempt to avoid uncertainty over the dates of past events by using a cycle which comprehended all others and which was independent of calendrial systems. Scaliger adopted a cycle of 7,980 years, and expressed any date as the number of consecutive days which had elapsed since the mean noon of January 1, 4713 B.C.—a date of origin conveniently before October 4, 4004 B.C., the ecclesiastically authorized date of Creation. Although the Julian date is now nearing the two and a half million mark, it is of great value in astronomy, especially when recording the light fluctuations of variable stars. Scaliger called the days of his period 'Julian days' in memory of his father, Julius Caesar Scaliger. He was a great Greek and Hebrew scholar, spent most of his life in France and Holland, and had no part in Pope Gregory's calendar reform.

Germany adopted the Gregorian calendar in 1699, Denmark followed suit a year later, but England kept aloof until 1752. By this time the equinox on the Julian basis was falling on March 25, and therefore eleven days out of step with France and most of Europe. In this country the position was further complicated by the use of two calendars. The civil year began on March 25, and the historical year on January 1, so that dates like March 24, 175$\frac{1}{2}$ were not uncommon, the top figure indicating the civil and the bottom figure the historical year.

The adoption of the new calendar in England was due largely to the efforts of the Earls of Chesterfield and Macclesfield, assisted by the then Astronomer Royal, James Bradley. Since eleven days had to be dropped from the calendar, the month of September 1752 contained only nineteen days. A change of this nature naturally put people to no small inconvenience, and many among the working-classes complained that they had been robbed of eleven days. Others were scandalized at what they regarded to be an irreligious meddling with the sacred festivals of Christmas and Easter. By way of protest one old couple in a country town continued to observe Good Friday on the old day, walked to church in their 'Sunday-best', and finding no admittance there, solemnly returned to celebrate the service at home. On the new and spurious

Good Friday they celebrated the end of their Lent with merriment and feasting. But there were some days of comfort, for between 1752 and 1800 the old and new Easter Days coincided on eighteen occasions. Faithful Catholics were assured that creation would obey the papal mandate. Cattle prostrated themselves on the new Christmas Eve, twigs budded, and images of the saints continued to weep and bleed on the proper days and according to the new style. In England the blossoming of the famous Glastonbury thorn was looked for with some anxiety, but needlessly, for the co-operative bush flowered just before Christmas Day of the new style.

No one who has studied the Gregorian calendar in even the smallest way can deny that it has many inconveniences. All of us are aware that the days of the week vary in different months and in the same months of different years. An essentially week-day anniversary can occur on a Sunday, Christmas Day wanders among the days of the week, and Easter arrives sometimes in March and sometimes in April. Only once every twenty-eight years does the calendar of any one year exactly reproduce itself. The inequality of the calendar months, a legacy of the old Julian calendar, means that the quarters and half-years are unequal. This adds an unnecessary complication to reckonings in commerce and business, for the payment of salaries, pensions, rents, and interests are often arranged on a monthly, quarterly, or half-yearly basis.

The defects of the calendar, together with ways of correcting them, have been discussed from time to time at various international conferences. In 1922 the International Astronomical Union convened a special commission which approved certain changes, one of which entailed keeping a perpetual calendar of fifty-two weeks plus one or two blank days. In the following year the League of Nations arranged discussions on calendar problems at which ecclesiastical representatives expressed no objection to the introduction of a fixed Easter. In this connection the first Sunday in April was shown to possess singular advantages. In the

Q

first place, it deviates but little from the day of the event commemorated, namely, Friday, April 7, A.D. 30 or April 3, A.D. 33, and secondly, it promises fair spring weather for those who regard Easter solely as a holiday period. Christmas likewise could be shifted to one or two blank days at the end of each year of 364 days, for only pagan considerations identify the date of the Nativity with that of the winter solstice. For those who wish to conform to tradition by celebrating Christ's birthday on December 25, the one or two blank days could alternatively be kept as 'World's Days' or universal public holidays. These and other considerations are now the earnest concern of The International World Calendar Association, an organization which exists solely for the purpose of rectifying the many outstanding disadvantages of the Gregorian system.

BIBLIOGRAPHY

ASTRONOMY

Abetti, G., *The History of Astronomy*, 1954
Allen, R. H., *Star-Names and their Meanings*, 1899
Armitage, A., *Sun, Stand Thou Still*, 1947
Bensaude, J., *Histoire de la Science Nautique Portugaise à l'Époque des Grandes Découvertes*, 1914
Berry, A., *A Short History of Astronomy*, 1898
Brennand, W., *Hindu Astronomy*, 1896
Brown, B., *Astronomical Maps, Atlases and Charts*, 1932
Chambers, G. F., *The Story of Comets*, 1909
Davidson, M., *The Stars and the Mind*, 1947
Doig, P., *A Concise History of Astronomy*, 1950
Dreyer, J. L. E., *History of the Planetary Systems from Thales to Kepler*, 1906
Eisler, R., *The Royal Art of Astrology*, 1946
Flammarion, C., *Astronomical Myths*, 1877
Grant, R., *History of Physical Astronomy*, 1852
Guillaume, A., *The World of Comets*, 1877
Hardy, Rev. T., *Moon Lore*, 1885
Heath, Sir T. L., *Greek Astronomy*, 1932
Hellman, C. D., *The Comet of 1577: Its Place in the History of Astronomy*, 1944
Johnson, F. R., *Astronomical Thought in Renaissance England*, 1937
King, H. C., *The History of the Telescope*, 1955
Lamb, J., *The Phenomena and Diosemeia of Aratus*, 1848
Langdon, S., and Fotheringham, J. K., *The Venus Tablets of Ammizaduga*, 1928
Lewis, Sir G. C., *An Historical Survey of the Astronomy of the Ancients* 1862
Lockyer, J. N., *The Dawn of Astronomy*, 1894
Maunder, E. W., *The Royal Observatory Greenwich*, 1900
   The Astronomy of the Bible, 1908
Menon, C. P. S., *Early Astronomy and Cosmology*, 1932
Michel, H., *Traité de l'Astrolabe*, 1947
Neugebauer, O. (edit.), *Astronomical Cuneiform Texts*, 3 vols., 1955
Orr, M. A., *Dante and the Early Astronomers*, 1913

Piazzi-Smyth, C., *Life and Work at the Great Pyramid*, 1867
Pingré, A. G., *Cométographie: ou Traité Historique et Théorique des Cometès*, 2 vols., 1783–1784
Schiaparelli, G. V., *Astronomy in the Old Testament*, 1905
Thorndike, Lynn, *The Sphere of Sacrobosco and its Commentators*, 1949
   Latin Treatises on Comets between 1238 and 1368 A.D., 1951
Webb, E. J., *The Names of the Stars*, 1952

BIOGRAPHY

Armitage, A., *Copernicus, the Founder of Modern Astronomy*, 1938
Ball, J. M., *Andreas Vesalius, Reformer of Anatomy*, 1910
Baumgardt, C., *Johannes Kepler: Life and Letters*, 1952
Bell, E. E., *Christian Huygens*, 1947
Callus, D. A. (edit.), *Robert Grosseteste, Scholar and Bishop*, 1955
Chesterton, G. K., *Chaucer*, 1954
Crombie, A. C., *Robert Grosseteste and the Origins of Experimental Science*, 1953
Dreyer, J. L. E., *Tycho Brahe*, 1890
Easton, S. C., *Roger Bacon*, 1952
Farrington, B., *Francis Bacon, Philosopher of Industrial Science*, 1951
Gade, J. A., *The Life and Times of Tycho Brahe*, 1947
Heath, T. L., *Aristarchus of Samos*, 1913
Mac Pike, E. F., *Correspondence and Papers of Edmund Halley*, 1932
More, L. T., *Isaac Newton, a Biography*, 1934
   The Life and Works of the Honourable Robert Boyle, 1944
Morley, H., *Jerome Cardan*, 2 vols., 1854

CALENDAR AND TIME-KEEPING

Achelis, E., *Of Time and the Calendar*, 1955
Budge, F. A. Wallis, *The Decree of Canopus*, 1904
Milham, W. I., *Time and Timekeepers*, 1923
Panth, B. D., *Consider the Calendar*, 1944
Watkins, H., *Time Counts: The Story of the Calendar*, 1954
Wood, E. J., *Curiosities of Clocks and Watches*, 1866

CHEMISTRY AND ALCHEMY

Ferchl, F., and Süssenguth, A., *A Pictorial History of Chemistry*, 1939
Givry, Grillot de, *Witchcraft, Magic and Alchemy*, 1931
Holmyard, E. J., *Makers of Chemistry*, 1931

BIBLIOGRAPHY

Partington, J. R., *A Short History of Chemistry*, 1948
Read, J., *Prelude to Chemistry*, 1939
   Humour and Humanism in Chemistry, 1947
   The Alchemist in Life, Literature and Art, 1947
Taylor, F. S., *The Alchemists, Founders of Modern Chemistry*, 1949

GEOGRAPHY

Beazley, C. R., *The Dawn of Modern Geography*, 3 vols., 1897–1907
Bunbury, E. H., *History of Ancient Geography*, 2 vols., 1879
Crone, G. R., *Maps and their Makers*, 1953
Kimble, G. H., *Geography in the Middle Ages*, 1938
Stevens, H., *Ptolemy's Geography*, 1908
Thomson, J. O., *History of Ancient Geography*, 1948
Tooley, R. V., *Maps and Map-Makers*, 1952
Warmington, E. H., *Greek Geography*, 1934

HISTORY AND ARCHAEOLOGY

Arnold, Sir T. W., and Guillaume, A. (eds.), *The Legacy of Islam*, 1931
Bailey, C. (edit.), *The Legacy of Rome*, 1935
Burckhardt, J., *The Age of Constantine the Great*, 1949
Ceram, C. W., *Gods, Graves and Scholars*, 1954
Contenau, G., *Everyday Life in Babylon and Assyria*, 1954
Crump, C. G., and Jacob, E. F. (eds.), *The Legacy of the Middle Ages*, 1932
Edwards, I. E. S., *The Pyramids of Egypt*, 1952
Fisher, H. A. L., *A History of Europe* (3 vols.), 1935
Frankfort, H., *The Birth of Civilization in the Near East*, 1951
Glanville, S. R. K. (edit.), *The Legacy of Egypt*, 1942
Grinsell, L. V., *The Ancient Burial Grounds of England*, 1953
Haydn, H., *The Counter-Renaissance*, 1950
Hitti, P. K., *History of the Arabs*, 1937
Hrozny, B., *Ancient History of Western Asia, India and Crete*, 1954
King, L. W., *The History of Sumer and Akkad*, 1916
Lewis, B., *The Arabs in History*, 1954
Livingstone, Sir R. W. (edit.), *The Legacy of Greece*, 1942
Murray, M. A., *The Splendour that was Egypt*, 1949
O'Leary, de Lacy, *Arabia before Muhammed*, 1927
Prestage, E., *The Portuguese Pioneers*, 1933
Rose, H. J., *Primitive Culture in Greece*, 1925

Southern, R. W., *The Making of the Middle Ages*, 1953
Tarn, W. W., *Alexander the Great*, 1948
Weigall, A., *The Life and Times of Akhnaton*, 1923
Woolley, Sir C. L., *The Sumerians*, 1928
  Ur Excavations, 1939

MATHEMATICS

Ball, W. W. R., *A Short History of Mathematics*, 1940
Bell, E. T., *Men of Mathematics*, 1937
  The Development of Mathematics, 1945
Cajori, F., *A History of Mathematics*, 1924
Heath, Sir T. L., *A History of Greek Mathematics*, 2 vols., 1921
Kline, M., *Mathematics in Western Culture*, 1954
Smith, D. E., *History of Mathematics*, 2 vols., 1923
Struik, D. J., *A Concise History of Mathematics*, 1948
Taylor, E. G. R., *The Mathematical Practitioners of Tudor and Stuart England*, 1954
Waerden, B. L. van der, *Science Awakening*, 1954

MEDICINE

Browne, E. G., *Arabian Medicine*, 1921
Elgood, C., *History of Persian Medicine*, 1935
Guthrie, D., *A History of Medicine*, 1947
James, R. Ruston, *Studies in the History of Ophthalmology in England prior to the year 1800*, 1933
Neuburger, M., *History of Medicine*, 1910
Robinson, V., *The Story of Medicine*, 1931
Singer, C., *Greek Biology and Greek Medicine*, 1922
  A Short History of Medicine, 1928
Sorsby, A., *A Short History of Ophthalmology*, 1948
Withington, E. T., *Medical History from the Earliest Times*, 1894

RELIGION AND MYTHOLOGY

Dawson, C., *Religion and the Rise of Western Culture*, 1950
Everett, J. R., *Religion in Human Experience*, 1952
Frazer, Sir J. G., *Folk Lore in the Old Testament*, 1923
  The Worship of Nature, 1926
  Magic and Religion, 1944
Gowen, H. H., *A History of Religion*, 1934

Graves, R., *The White Goddess*, 1954
  The Greek Myths, 1955
Guthrie, W. K. C., *The Greeks and their Gods*, 1950
James, E. O., *Comparative Religion*, 1938
Mercer, S. A. B., *The Religion of Ancient Egypt*, 1949
Pinches, T. G., *Religion of Babylonia and Assyria*, 1906
Reinach, S., *Orpheus, a History of Religion*, 1931
Rose, H. J., *A Handbook of Greek Mythology*, 1953
Russell, Bertrand A. W., *A History of Western Philosophy*, 1946
Sayce, A. H., *The Religions of Ancient Egypt and Babylonia*, 1902
Sherwood Fox, *Greek and Roman Mythology*, 1930
Smith, Homer W., *Man and his Gods*, 1953
Spence, Lewis, *An Encyclopaedia of Occultism*, 1920
White, A. D., *A History of the Warfare of Science with Theology*, 1895;
  new edition, 1955

SCIENCE AND ITS PHILOSOPHY

Bernal, J. D., *Science in History*, 1954
Butterfield, H., *The Origins of Modern Science (1300–1800)*, 1949
Collingwood, R. G., *The Idea of Nature*, 1944
Cornford, F. M., *The Laws of Motion in Ancient Thought*, 1931
Dampier, Sir W. C., *A History of Science and its Relations with Philosophy and Religion*, 1946
Farrington, B., *Greek Science*, 2 vols., 1906
  Science in Antiquity, 1936
Gunther, R. W. T., *Early Science in Oxford*, 14 vols., 1923–1945
Hall, A. R., *The Scientific Revolution (1500–1800)*, 1954
Haskins, C. H., *Studies in the History of Medieval Science*, 1924
Heiberg, J. L., *Mathematics and Physical Science in Classical Antiquity*, 1922
Mason, S. F., *A History of the Sciences*, 1953
Neugebauer, O., *The Technical Arts and Sciences of the Ancients*, 1930
  The Exact Sciences in Antiquity, 1951
Nordenskiöld, E., *The History of Biology*, 1927
Pledge, H. T., *Science Since 1500*, 1940
Sarton, G., *Introduction to the History of Science*, vol. 1, 1927
  Ancient Science to Epicurus, 1952
  A History of Science through the Golden Age of Greece, 1933
Sherrington, Sir C., *Man on his Nature*, 1946
Singer, C., *From Magic to Science*, 1928

Singer, C., Holmyard, E. J., and Hall, A. R., *A History of Technology*, 1954

Thorndike, Lynn, *A History of Magic and Experimental Science during the First Thirteen Centuries of our Era*, 2 vols., 1923

Wolff, A., *A History of Science, Technology and Philosophy in the Sixteenth and Seventeenth Centuries*, 1950

INDEX

247